Cahier d'exercices

Julie Green

Heinemann
Part of Pearson

Mon autoportrait (pages 8–9)

1 Separate out the sentences. Put a tick in the box if the person likes something and a cross if they don't like something.

1 J'aimelamusiquec'estcool.

2 J'aimelerugbyc'estgénial.

3 Jen'aimepasl'injusticec'estnul.

4 J'aimeleschatsetaussileschiens.

5 J'aimelesinsectesmaisjen'aimepaslesreptiles.

1 ______________________ ☐

2 ______________________ ☐

3 ______________________ ☐

4 ______________________ ☐

5 ______________________ ☐

2 Write sentences like those in exercise 1 to match these pictures.

la musique	*les jeux vidéo*
le foot	*les animaux*
les reptiles	*les maths*

Remember to use connectives.

et *and*
aussi *also*
mais *but*

1 ______________________

2 ______________________

3 ______________________

4 ______________________

2 Mon kit de survie (pages 10–11)

1 Work out the missing word in each sentence below and complete the crossword.

barre de céréales	*de*
lunettes de soleil	*j'ai*
portemonnaie	*gourde*
appareil photo	*pas*
jeux vidéo	*kleenex*
magazine	*chips*
je n'ai pas	*portable*

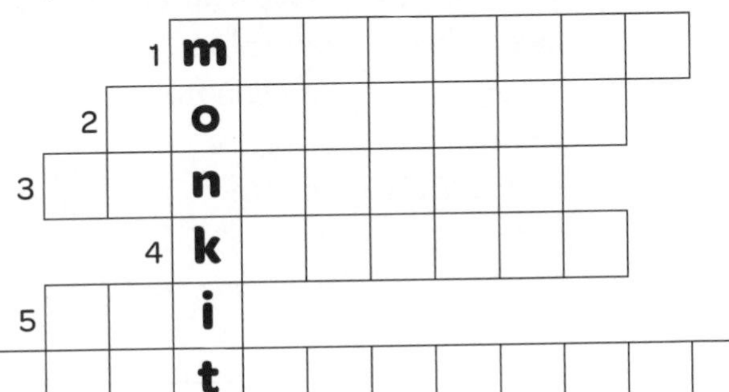

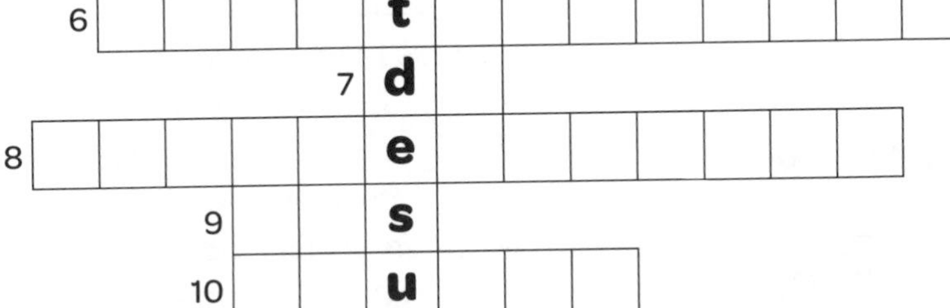

j'ai ...
I have ...
je n'ai pas de ...
I don't have a/any ...

1 J'ai un + 

2 Je n'ai pas de + 

3 Non,  _____ de clé.

4 J'ai des + 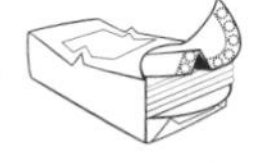

5  _____ un sac.

6 J'ai des + 

7 Je n'ai pas _____ miroir.

8 J'ai un

9 Je n'ai _____ de clé USB.

10 J'ai une 

11 Je n'ai pas de + 

12 J'ai des + 

13 J'ai des + 

14 J'ai une +

2 Write a sentence to match each group of pictures.

Example: Dans mon sac, j'ai un MP3 mais je n'ai pas de calculatrice.

1 

2 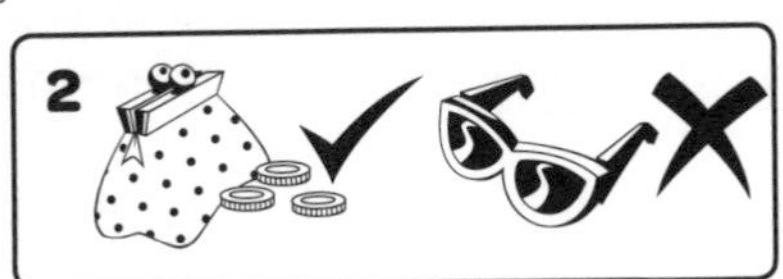

3

3 Comment je me vois (pages 12–13)

1 Read the two texts and then:

- underline the four masculine adjectives
- circle the three feminine adjectives
- highlight the two adjectives which don't change.

Studio Grammaire

Most adjectives have a different feminine form:

masculine	**feminine**
intelligent	*intelligent**e***
curieux	*curieu**se***

but some stay the same:

drôle	*drôle*
modeste	*modeste*

Salut! Je suis Hoblegobble. Je suis assez intelligent et je suis gentil. Je suis très poli mais je ne suis pas très généreux. J'aime le sport. C'est génial. Mais je n'aime pas le racisme. C'est nul.

Je m'appelle Rose. J'aime les animaux et aussi les araignées. Aimer les animaux, c'est très important pour moi. Je suis assez branchée et je suis très curieuse. Ah, et je suis modeste, aussi. Je ne suis pas très intelligente et je ne suis pas drôle.

2 Write H for Hoblegobble or R for Rose.

Who ...

1 is quite trendy? ☐
2 likes sport? ☐
3 is not very generous? ☐
4 is modest? ☐
5 is not very intelligent? ☐
6 likes spiders? ☐
7 is very curious? ☐
8 is very polite? ☐

3 Write a few sentences like those in exercise 1 using the following notes.

____
____
____
____
____
____
____

charmant(e) *cool*
modeste *grand(e)*
curieux/curieuse

je suis	*I am*
je ne suis pas	*I'm not*
assez	*quite*
très	*very*

4 Et les autres? (pages 14–15)

1 Write the letter of the picture each sentence is describin

a **b** **c**

1. Mon ami s'appelle Mathéo et il aime le sport. ☐
2. Elle est très grande. ☐
3. Il a les cheveux courts et frisés. ☐
4. Mon amie s'appelle Clara et elle aime les animaux. ☐
5. Mon amie s'appelle Élodie et elle n'aime pas l'injustice. ☐
6. Elle a les cheveux longs et raides. ☐
7. Il est assez grand. ☐
8. Il a les cheveux longs et frisés. ☐
9. Elle est très petite. ☐
10. Mon ami s'appelle Luc. Il n'aime pas le sport mais il aime la musique. ☐

Remember what *il* and *elle* mean? They should help you to match the sentences to the picture.

2 Unjumble and write out each sentence to describe the footballer Alex Song.

cheveux longs a les et frisés Il ______

assez Il grand est ______

Il marron a yeux les ______

modeste Il est est branché et il très aussi ______

aime pas la mais il n'aime Il le racisme musique ______

______

3 Adapt each sentence in exercise 2 to describe another famous person.

Remember to use these 'little' words:

assez = *quite* ***et*** = *and* ***mais*** = *but*

très = *very* ***aussi*** = *also*

Il est hypercool (pages 16–17)

1 **Write the verbs from the box in the correct part of the diagram. Verbs that could go with both *je* and *il/elle* should go into the middle section.**

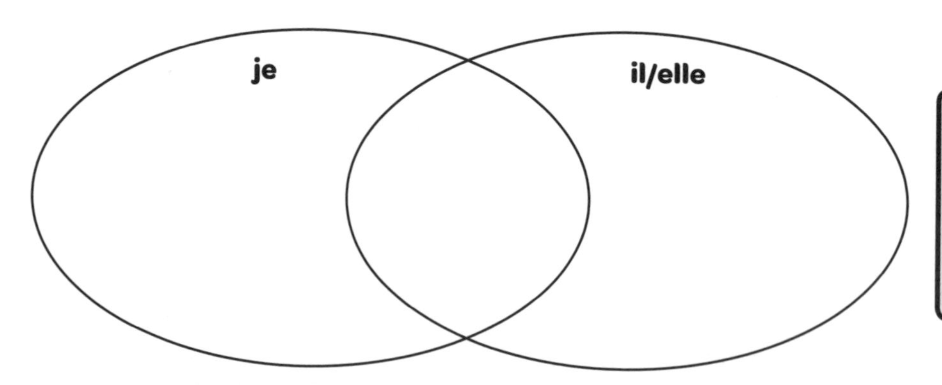

ai joue est m'appelle s'appelle suis a chante aime

Studio Grammaire

-er verbs	avoir	être	s'appeler
Je chante	J'ai	Je suis	Je m'appelle
Il/Elle chante	Il/Elle a	Il/Elle est	Il/Elle s'appelle

2 **Complete the two texts with words from the box.**

ai est joue a suis aime chante j'aime s'appelle m'appelle

Il __________ Rocky Guy.
Il __________ cool et beau.
Il __________ le metal.
Il __________ et il joue de la guitare.
Il __________ beaucoup de talent.

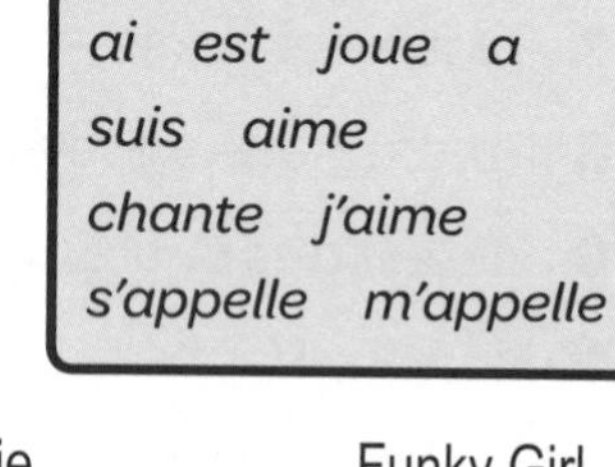

Moi, je __________ Funky Girl.
J'__________ les cheveux courts et noirs et je __________ de taille moyenne.
__________ le funk et je chante avec les Cool Girls.
Je __________ de la batterie.

3 **Imagine you are the musician in the picture. Adapt Funky Girl's text from exercise 2 to write a few sentences.**

Révision 1

1 Crack the code for these sentences. Try to add accents in the right places.

a (10, 5) (13′, 1, 16, 16, 5, 12, 12, 5) (15, 3, 5, 1, 14, 5)

Je m'appelle Océane.

b (10′, 1, 9, 13, 5) (12, 1) (13, 21, 19, 9, 17, 21, 5) (5, 20) (12, 5, 19) (13, 1, 14, 7, 1, 19).

____

c (10, 5) (14′, 1, 9, 13, 5) (16, 1, 19) (12, 5) (18, 1, 3, 9, 19, 13, 5).

____

d (10′, 1, 9) (21, 14, 5) (2, 1, 18, 18, 5) (4, 5) (3, 5, 18, 5, 1, 12, 5, 19) (5, 20) (21, 14, 5) (3, 12, 5) (21, 19, 2).

____

e (3′, 5, 19, 20) (12, 5, 15, 14, 1) (12, 5, 23, 9, 19). (5, 12, 12, 5) (5, 19, 20) (3, 8, 1, 14, 20, 5, 21, 19, 5).

____

2 Match the answers in exercise 1 to these questions.

1 Qu'est-ce que tu as dans ton sac? ☐
2 Qu'est-ce que tu aimes? ☐
3 C'est qui, ta star préférée? ☐
4 Tu t'appelles comment? ☐
5 Qu'est-ce que tu n'aimes pas? ☐

Qu'est-ce que ...?	*What ...?*
Qui ...?	*Who ...?*
Comment ...?	*What/How ...?*

3 Answer the questions in exercise 2, giving your own answers.

1 **Read the penfriend forum entries.**

Les correspondants

Salut! Je suis française, j'ai douze ans et j'habite à Strasbourg en France. J'aime le sport, surtout le tennis et le hockey, mais je déteste les chiens! J'attends ta réponse. Bisous Sonia

Salut! J'adore la musique et je joue du piano. J'habite au Canada et j'ai onze ans. Je cherche un correspondant qui habite en France. J'ai les cheveux courts et roux et j'ai les yeux bleus. Répondez s'il vous plaît! Hugo

Je m'appelle Brad. Je suis américain et j'habite à Philadelphie. J'ai quatorze ans et je cherche un correspondant pour améliorer mon français. J'aime jouer au foot et aussi, j'adore jouer de la batterie. Répondre svp.

Je m'appelle Justine et j'ai quinze ans. Je cherche un correspondant anglais. J'aime la musique rock, les films (mais pas les films d'horreur) et les chats! Je cherche un(e) correspondant(e) qui a quinze ou seize ans. Réponds-moi vite!

Who would be an ideal penfriend for each of these people?

1 I'm English and I'm 15. ________
2 I'm female and I love playing sports. ________
3 I'm French and I adore red hair! ________
4 I love going to the cinema. ________
5 I'm 12 and I don't like animals. ________
6 I live in France and I'm musical. I'm 11. ________
7 I like sport and music. ________
8 I love animals and I'm 16. ________

2 **Can you work out the new words in the entries? You can often work out the meaning of a new word by:**

- noticing the similarity with an English word
- looking at the rest of the sentence
- using common sense and logic.

What do you think these expressions mean? (they are underlined in the forum)

1 surtout ________
2 ta réponse your ________
3 un correspondant ________
4 américain ________
5 améliorer mon français to ________ my French
6 je cherche ________
7 les films d'horreur ________

J'avance

1 Record your levels for Module 1.

2 Look at the level descriptors on pages 60–61 and set your targets for Module 2.

3 Fill in what you need to do to achieve these targets.

Listening	I have reached Level ______ in **Listening**. In Module 2, I want to reach Level ______. I need to ______________________
Speaking	I have reached Level ______ in **Speaking**. In Module 2, I want to reach Level ______. I need to ______________________
Reading	I have reached Level ______ in **Reading**. In Module 2, I want to reach Level ______. I need to ______________________
Writing	I have reached Level ______ in **Writing**. In Module 2, I want to reach Level ______. I need to ______________________

Mon autoportrait • *My self-portrait*

les animaux (m pl)	*animals*
les araignées (f pl)	*spiders*
la capoeira	*a Brazilian dance*
les chats (m pl)	*cats*
les chiens (m pl)	*dogs*
le cinéma	*cinema*
les consoles de jeux (f pl)	*games consoles*
la danse	*dancing*
le foot	*football*
les gâteaux (m pl)	*cakes*
le hard rock	*hard rock*
l'injustice (f)	*injustice*
les insectes (m pl)	*insects*
les jeux vidéo (m pl)	*video games*
les livres (m pl)	*books*
la musique	*music*
les mangas (m pl)	*mangas*
les maths (f pl)	*maths*
les pizzas (f pl)	*pizzas*
la poésie	*poetry*
le racisme	*racism*
le rap	*rap*
le reggae	*reggae*
les reptiles (m pl)	*reptiles*
le roller	*roller-skating*
le rugby	*rugby*
le skate	*skateboarding*
les spaghettis (m pl)	*spaghetti*
le sport	*sport*
la tecktonik	*tecktonik (dance)*
la télé	*TV*
le tennis	*tennis*
le théâtre	*theatre, drama*
les voyages (m pl)	*journeys*
la violence	*violence*

Les opinions • *Opinions*

j'aime	*I like*
je n'aime pas	*I don't like*
Tu aimes ...?	*Do you like ...?*
il/elle aime	*he/she likes*
Oui, j'aime ça.	*Yes, I like that.*
Non, je n'aime pas ça.	*No, I don't like that.*
Tu es d'accord?	*Do you agree?*
Je suis d'accord.	*I agree.*
Je ne suis pas d'accord.	*I don't agree.*
C'est ...	*It's ...*
génial	*great*
cool	*cool*
bien	*good*
ennuyeux	*boring*
nul	*rubbish*
essentiel	*essential*
important	*important*
Ce n'est pas bien.	*It's not good.*

Mon kit de survie • *My survival kit*

j'ai	*I have*
je n'ai pas de	*I don't have*
tu as	*you have*
il/elle a	*he/she has*
un appareil photo	*a camera*
une barre de céréales	*a cereal bar*
un bâton de colle	*a gluestick*
des chips (f pl)	*crisps*
des clés (f pl)	*keys*
une clé USB	*a memory stick*
une gourde	*a water bottle*
des kleenex (m pl)	*tissues*
des lunettes de soleil (f pl)	*sunglasses*
un magazine	*a magazine*
un miroir	*a mirror*

contd.

un portable	*a mobile phone*
un portemonnaie	*a purse*
un paquet de mouchoirs	*a packet of tissues*
un sac	*a bag*
des surligneurs fluo (m pl)	*fluorescent highlighters*
une trousse	*a pencil case*

Moi et les autres • *Me and other people*

je suis	*I am*
je ne suis pas	*I am not*
tu es	*you are*
il/elle s'appelle	*he/she is called*
il/elle est	*he/she is*
beau/belle	*good-looking*
branché(e)	*trendy*
charmant(e)	*charming*
cool	*cool*
curieux/curieuse	*curious*
de taille moyenne	*average height*
drôle	*funny*
généreux/généreuse	*generous*
gentil(le)	*nice*
grand(e)	*tall*
impatient(e)	*impatient*
intelligent(e)	*intelligent*
modeste	*modest*
petit(e)	*small*
poli(e)	*polite*

Les yeux et les cheveux • *Eyes and hair*

j'ai	*I have*
tu as	*you have*
il/elle a	*he/she has*
mon ami(e) a	*my friend has*
J'ai...	*I have...*
les yeux bleus	*blue eyes*
les yeux verts	*green eyes*
les yeux gris	*grey eyes*
les yeux marron	*brown eyes*
J'ai...	*I have...*
les cheveux longs	*long hair*
les cheveux courts	*short hair*
les cheveux mi-longs	*medium-length hair*
frisés/raides	*curly/straight*
blonds/bruns	*blond/brown*
noirs/roux	*black/red*

Les musiciens • *Musicians*

Il/Elle joue ...	*He/She plays ...*
de la batterie	*the drums*
de la guitare	*the guitar*
Il/Elle chante.	*He/She sings.*
Il/Elle a beaucoup de talent.	*He/She has a lot of talent.*

Les mots essentiels • *High-frequency words*

et	*and*
aussi	*also*
mais	*but*
très	*very*
assez	*quite*
toujours	*always*
Qu'est-ce que ...?	*What ...?*
Qui ...?	*Who ...?*

1 Mes matières (pages 28–29)

1 Draw lines to match the symbols with the phrases.

2 
3 
4 
5 

a J'aime **b** J'aime assez **c** Je n'aime pas **d** J'adore **e** Je déteste

2 Look at the table and read the sentences below. Who does each one describe?

Camille	☺☺	☺	😐	☹	☺	☹☹	☺☺
Enzo	☺	😐	☹	☺	☹☹	☺☺	😐
Chloé	☹	☺	☺☺	☺☺	☹	☺	☹☹
Théo	☹☹	☹	☺	☺	😐	☹☹	☺
Moi							

1. J'aime les arts plastiques mais je déteste la géo. ______
2. J'aime le français et le sport mais je n'aime pas les arts plastiques. ______
3. J'adore l'anglais et le théâtre mais je n'aime pas le français. ______
4. Je n'aime pas l'informatique mais j'adore l'EPS. ______
5. Je déteste l'anglais mais j'aime assez l'informatique. ______
6. J'aime l'anglais et le français et j'aime assez le théâtre. ______
7. Je n'aime pas l'anglais mais j'adore le français. C'est ma matière préférée. ______
8. J'aime les arts plastiques et j'aime aussi l'informatique. ______

3 Complete the table with your own opinions and then write three sentences.

______

______

______

C'est génial! (pages 30–31)

1 Work out the jumbled words and then write out the full e-mail.

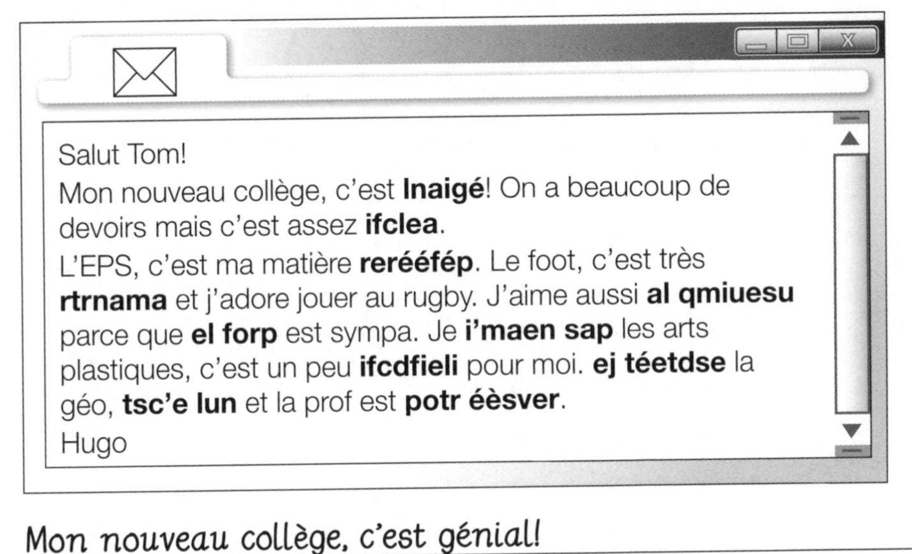

Salut Tom!
Mon nouveau collège, c'est **lnaigé**! On a beaucoup de devoirs mais c'est assez **ifclea**.
L'EPS, c'est ma matière **rerééfép**. Le foot, c'est très **rtrnama** et j'adore jouer au rugby. J'aime aussi **al qmiuesu** parce que **el forp** est sympa. Je **i'maen sap** les arts plastiques, c'est un peu **ifcdfieli** pour moi. **ej téetdse** la géo, **tsc'e lun** et la prof est **potr èèsver**.
Hugo

Mon nouveau collège, c'est génial!

______

______

______

______

______

2 Read the e-mail again and note in English what Hugo thinks of the following.

1 geography	teacher too strict	**5** art	______
2 his new school	______	**6** rugby	______
3 PE	______	**7** homework	______
4 music	______	**8** football	______

3 Imagine you've just moved schools. Write a similar e-mail using these symbols and words.

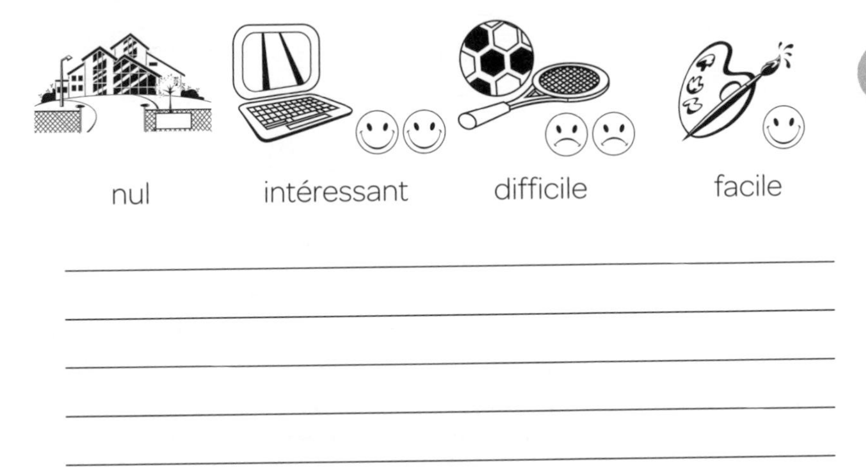

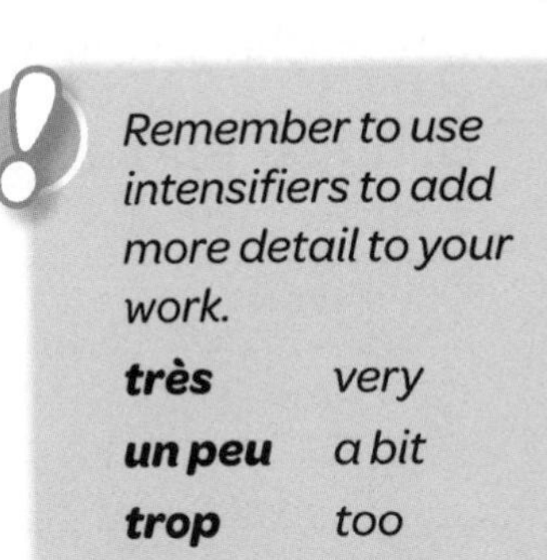

Remember to use intensifiers to add more detail to your work.

très	*very*
un peu	*a bit*
trop	*too*
assez	*quite*

______

______

______

______

______

1 **Find times in the wordsearch to match the times on the clocks.**

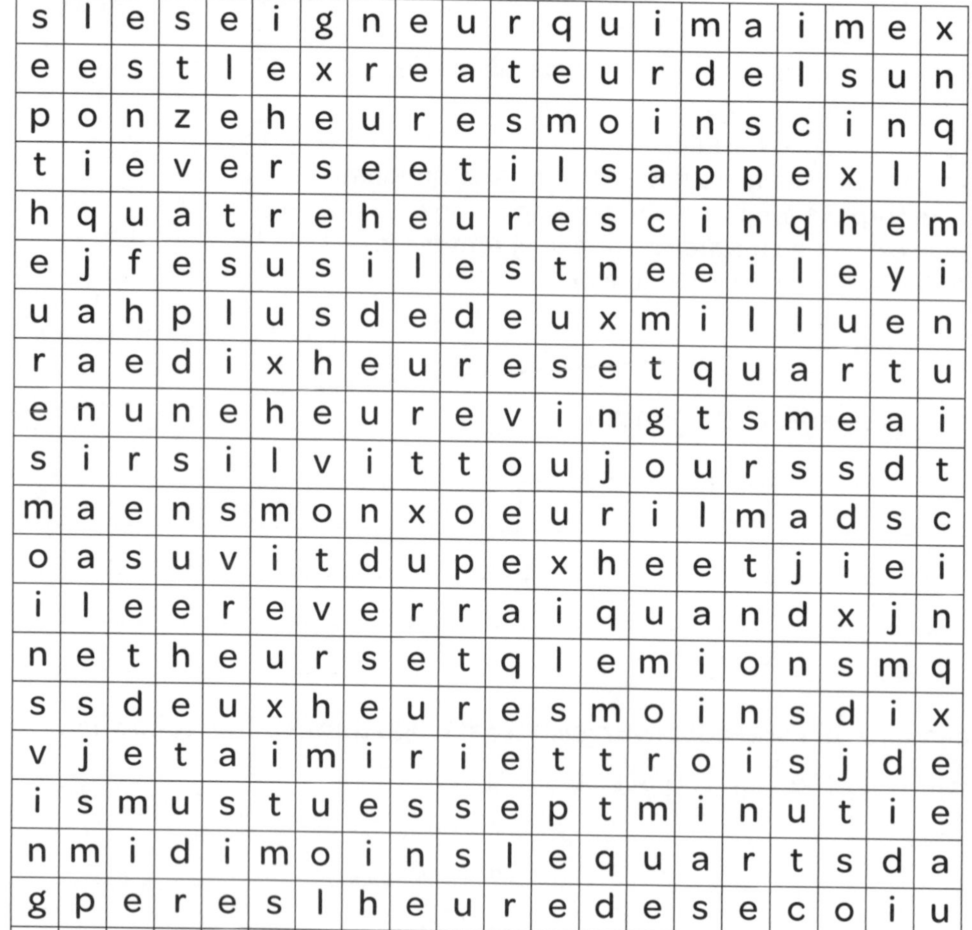

s	l	e	s	e	i	g	n	e	u	r	q	u	i	m	a	i	m	e	x
e	e	s	t	l	e	x	r	e	a	t	e	u	r	d	e	l	s	u	n
p	o	n	z	e	h	e	u	r	e	s	m	o	i	n	s	c	i	n	q
t	i	e	v	e	r	s	e	e	t	i	l	s	a	p	p	e	x	l	l
h	q	u	a	t	r	e	h	e	u	r	e	s	c	i	n	q	h	e	m
e	j	f	e	s	u	s	i	l	e	s	t	n	e	e	i	l	e	y	i
u	a	h	p	l	u	s	d	e	d	e	u	x	m	i	l	l	u	e	n
r	a	e	d	i	x	h	e	u	r	e	s	e	t	q	u	a	r	t	u
e	n	u	n	e	h	e	u	r	e	v	i	n	g	t	s	m	e	a	i
s	i	r	s	i	l	v	i	t	t	o	u	j	o	u	r	s	s	d	t
m	a	e	n	s	m	o	n	x	o	e	u	r	i	l	m	a	d	s	c
o	a	s	u	v	i	t	d	u	p	e	x	h	e	e	t	j	i	e	i
i	l	e	e	r	e	v	e	r	r	a	i	q	u	a	n	d	x	j	n
n	e	t	h	e	u	r	s	e	t	q	l	e	m	i	o	n	s	m	q
s	s	d	e	u	x	h	e	u	r	e	s	m	o	i	n	s	d	i	x
v	j	e	t	a	i	m	i	r	i	e	t	t	r	o	i	s	j	d	e
i	s	m	u	s	t	u	e	s	s	e	p	t	m	i	n	u	t	i	e
n	m	i	d	i	m	o	i	n	s	l	e	q	u	a	r	t	s	d	a
g	p	e	r	e	s	l	h	e	u	r	e	d	e	s	e	c	o	i	u
t	r	o	i	s	h	e	u	r	e	s	e	t	q	u	a	r	t	x	c

2 **Write French sentences to match these diary notes. Check your spellings on pages 20–21.**

Le lundi, j'ai musique à neuf heures et

Mon: music 9.00: maths 10.05
Tue: English 10.15: French 11.20
Wed: science 8.30: ICT 9.35
Thu: history 11.45: PE 12.30
Fri: drama 9.15: geography 10.35

lundi	*mercredi*	*vendredi*
mardi	*jeudi*	

1 Match the sentence halves to write captions for the story below the pictures.

1 On commence les
2 À la récré
3 On a quatre cours le matin
4 On finit les cours à
5 Je suis en section basket et on a un emploi
6 Après les cours on

a joue au basket. C'est génial!
b cours à huit heures dix.
c trois heures et demie.
d du temps différent.
e et deux cours l'après-midi.
f on bavarde et on rigole.

Salut, je suis Nathan! Mon collège est un peu différent. On est en section basket.

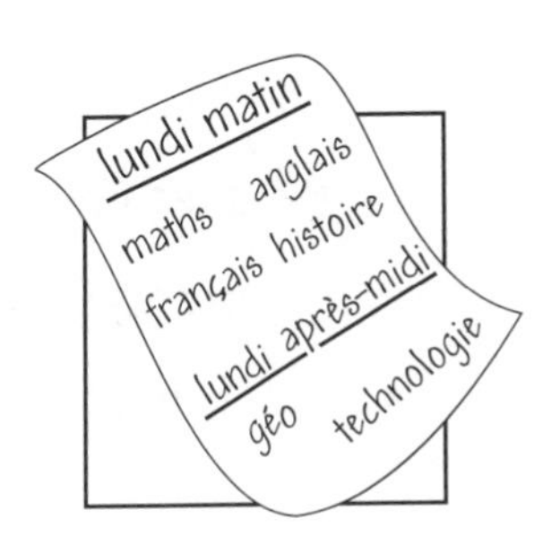

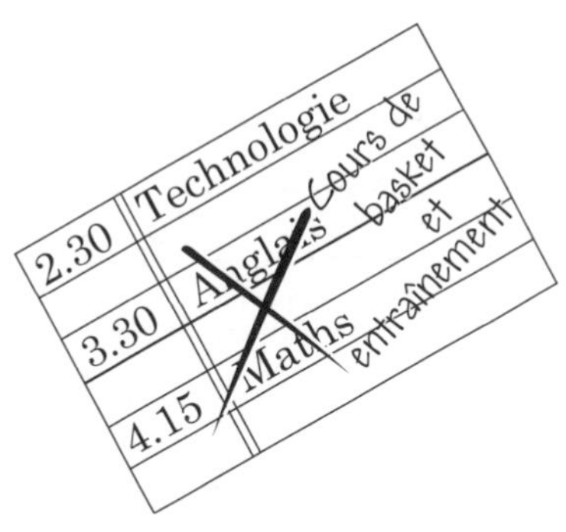

2 Complete the English summary of the story.

Nathan's school is a bit (1) ________. It has a specialism in (2) ________. Lessons start at (3) ________ and there are four lessons (4) ________ and two (5) ________. He finishes normal lessons at (6) ________ and then after that he (7) ________.

Miam-miam! (pages 36–37)

1 **Read the text, then complete the crossword below with the correct partitive (*du/de la/des*) and food item.**

Mes repas

Le matin, je mange (1) 

A midi, à la cantine, je mange

(5) avec (3)  et

comme dessert, (8). Miam-miam!

Le soir, à huit heures, je mange

(2)  avec (9) et (6) .

Après ça, je mange (7) 

et comme dessert, (4). Délicieux!

Studio Grammaire

To say **some**

masculine singular	feminine singular	plural
du	***de la***	***des***
yaourt	*mousse au chocolat*	*crudités*
poisson	*glace à la fraise*	*haricots verts*
fromage	*purée de pommes de terre*	*frites*
poulet	*pizza*	
steak haché	*tarte au citron*	

(Crossword — vertical word: d u s t e a k h a c h é)

1 ____ u ____
2 ____ s ____
3 ____ t ____
4 ____ e ____
5 ____ a ____
6 ____ h ____
7 ____ a ____
8 ____ c ____
9 ____ é ____

2 **Imagine you are Grace Gourmande. Write a text similar to the one above to describe your meals, using the symbols below.**

le matin	à la cantine	à huit heures

____

____

____

Révision 1

1 Choose one item from each column to form eight sentences which make sense.

A	B	C
Quelle	finit à	et quart.
Il est	heures	heures.
Il est midi	les cours	le matin.
Il est neuf	heure	à huit heures.
On commence	et	cantine.
On	huit	est-il?
On a	à la	demi.
On mange	quatre cours	quatre heures.

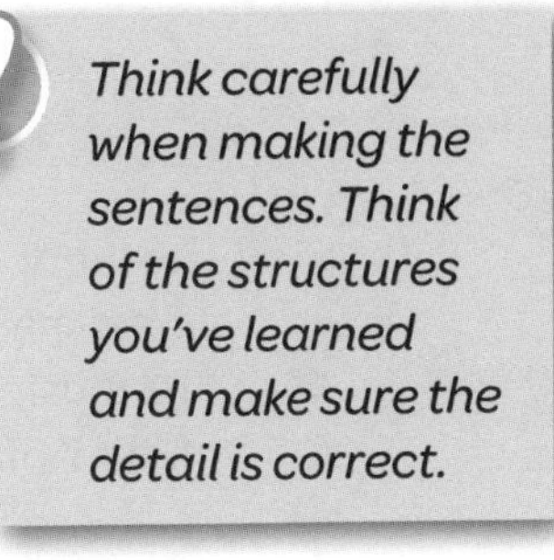

Think carefully when making the sentences. Think of the structures you've learned and make sure the detail is correct.

2 Answer these questions by adapting the sentences in exercise 1 to include your own details.

Dans ton collège, à quelle heure est-ce qu'on commence les cours?

On a combien de cours, le matin?

Et l'après-midi?

On mange où, à midi?

On finit à quelle heure?

1 **Read the poem aloud. Take care with your pronunciation and make sure the lines rhyme.**

Le lundi, c'est la rentrée et on commence avec musique.
C'est ma matière préférée, mais je déteste l'informatique.
La musique, c'est bien, la prof est toujours sympa
Mais l'informatique, c'est nul. Je n'aime pas ça.

Mon collège, c'est différent. On a des cours spécialisés.
On est en section «musique», on a des classes à horaires aménagés.
Le matin, on commence tôt, à sept heures et demie.
On a cours le matin puis on a musique tout l'après-midi.

Le matin, on étudie les maths, le français, l'informatique, l'histoire.
J'aime beaucoup l'anglais mais on a trop de devoirs.
L'après-midi, on chante, on joue d'un instrument.
On a chorale, on a orchestre, c'est toujours marrant!

2 **Work out or guess the meaning of these words and expressions.**

1 la rentrée ______________________
2 des cours spécialisés ______________________
3 tôt ______________________
4 tout l'après-midi ______________________
5 on joue d'un instrument ______________________
6 on a chorale ______________________
7 on a orchestre ______________________

You can often work out the meaning of a new word by:

- *noticing the similarity with an English word*
- *looking at the rest of the sentence*
- *having a sensible guess.*

3 **Read the poem again and:**

- underline any school subjects
- circle any opinions
- highlight times or times of day (e.g. morning, afternoon).

Then write three sentences in English to summarise what the poem is describing.

____

____

____

J'avance

1 **Record your levels for Module 2.**

2 **Look at the level descriptors on pages 60–61 and set your targets for Module 3.**

3 **Fill in what you need to do to achieve these targets.**

Listening	I have reached Level ____ in **Listening**. In Module 3, I want to reach Level ____. I need to ________________________________ ________________________________ ________________________________ ________________________________
Speaking Salut!	I have reached Level ____ in **Speaking**. In Module 3, I want to reach Level ____. I need to ________________________________ ________________________________ ________________________________ ________________________________
Reading	I have reached Level ____ in **Reading**. In Module 3, I want to reach Level ____. I need to ________________________________ ________________________________ ________________________________ ________________________________
Writing	I have reached Level ____ in **Writing**. In Module 3, I want to reach Level ____. I need to ________________________________ ________________________________ ________________________________ ________________________________

Les matières scolaires • *School subjects*

le français	*French*
le théâtre	*drama*
la géographie/la géo	*geography*
la musique	*music*
la technologie	*technology*
l'anglais (m)	*English*
l'EPS (f)	*PE*
l'histoire (f)	*history*
l'informatique (f)	*ICT*
les arts plastiques (m)	*art*
les mathématiques/maths (f)	*maths*
les sciences (f)	*science*

Les opinions • *Opinions*

Tu aimes/Est-ce que tu aimes ...?	*Do you like ...?*
J'aime ...	*I like ...*
J'aime beaucoup ...	*I like ... a lot.*
J'aime assez ...	*I quite like ...*
J'adore ...	*I love ...*
Je n'aime pas ...	*I don't like ...*
Je déteste ...	*I hate ...*
C'est ma matière préférée.	*It's my favourite subject.*
Moi aussi.	*Me too.*
T'es fou/folle.	*You're crazy.*

Les raisons • *Reasons*

C'est ...	*It's ...*
intéressant	*interesting*
ennuyeux	*boring*
facile	*easy*
difficile	*difficult*
génial	*great*
nul	*rubbish*

contd.

marrant	*fun/funny*
On a beaucoup de devoirs.	*We have a lot of homework.*
Le/La prof est sympa.	*The teacher is nice.*
Le/La prof est trop sévère.	*The teacher is too strict.*

Quelle heure est-il? • *What time is it?*

Il est ...	*It's ...*
huit heures	*eight o'clock*
huit heures dix	*ten past eight*
huit heures et quart	*quarter past eight*
huit heures et demie	*half past eight*
neuf heures moins vingt	*twenty to nine*
neuf heures moins le quart	*quarter to nine*
midi	*midday*
minuit	*midnight*
midi/minuit et demi	*half past twelve (midday/midnight)*

L'emploi du temps • *The timetable*

le lundi	*on Mondays*
le mardi	*on Tuesdays*
le mercredi	*on Wednesdays*
le jeudi	*on Thursdays*
le vendredi	*on Fridays*
À (neuf heures), j'ai (sciences).	*At (nine o'clock), I've got (science).*
le matin	*(in) the morning*
l'après-midi	*(in) the afternoon*
le mercredi après-midi	*on Wednesday afternoon*
la récréation/la récré	*breaktime*
le déjeuner	*lunch*

La journée scolaire • The school day

On a cours (le lundi).	*We have lessons (on Mondays).*
On n'a pas cours ...	*We don't have lessons ...*
On commence les cours à ...	*We start lessons at ...*
On a quatre cours le matin.	*We have four lessons in the morning.*
On étudie neuf matières.	*We study nine subjects.*
À la récré, on bavarde et on rigole.	*At break, we chat and have a laugh.*
On mange à la cantine.	*We eat in the canteen.*
On finit les cours à ...	*We finish lessons at ...*
On est fatigués.	*We are tired.*

Qu'est-ce que tu manges? • What do you eat?/What are you eating?

Je mange ...	*I eat/I'm eating ...*
du fromage	*cheese*
du poisson	*fish*
du poulet	*chicken*
du steak haché	*beefburger*
du yaourt	*yoghurt*
de la pizza	*pizza*
de la purée de pommes de terre	*mashed potatoes*
de la glace à la fraise	*strawberry ice-cream*
de la mousse au chocolat	*chocolate mousse*
de la tarte au citron	*lemon tart*

contd.

des crudités	*chopped, raw vegetables*
des frites	*chips*
des haricots verts	*green beans*
Bon appétit!	*Enjoy your meal!*

Les mots essentiels • High-frequency words

à	*at*
et	*and*
aussi	*also*
mais	*but*
très	*very*
trop	*too*
assez	*quite*
un peu	*a bit*
pourquoi?	*why?*
parce que	*because*
beaucoup (de)	*a lot (of)*
tous les jours	*every day*
aujourd'hui	*today*
pardon	*excuse me*
merci	*thank you*
Est-ce que (tu) ... ?	*Do (you) ... ?*
Qu'est-ce que (tu) ... ?	*What (do you) ... ?*
avec	*with*

1 Mon ordi et mon portable (pages 50–51)

1 **Find the sentences, then write them out next to the correct pictures.**

jesurfesurInternetjetchattesurMSNjeregardedesclipsvidéojeparleavecmescopainsjetéléchargedelamusique,j'envoiedesSMS

1 ______________________

2 ______________________

3 ______________________

4 ______________________

5 ______________________

6 ______________________

2 **Decode these six messages to say what technology you use, and how often.**

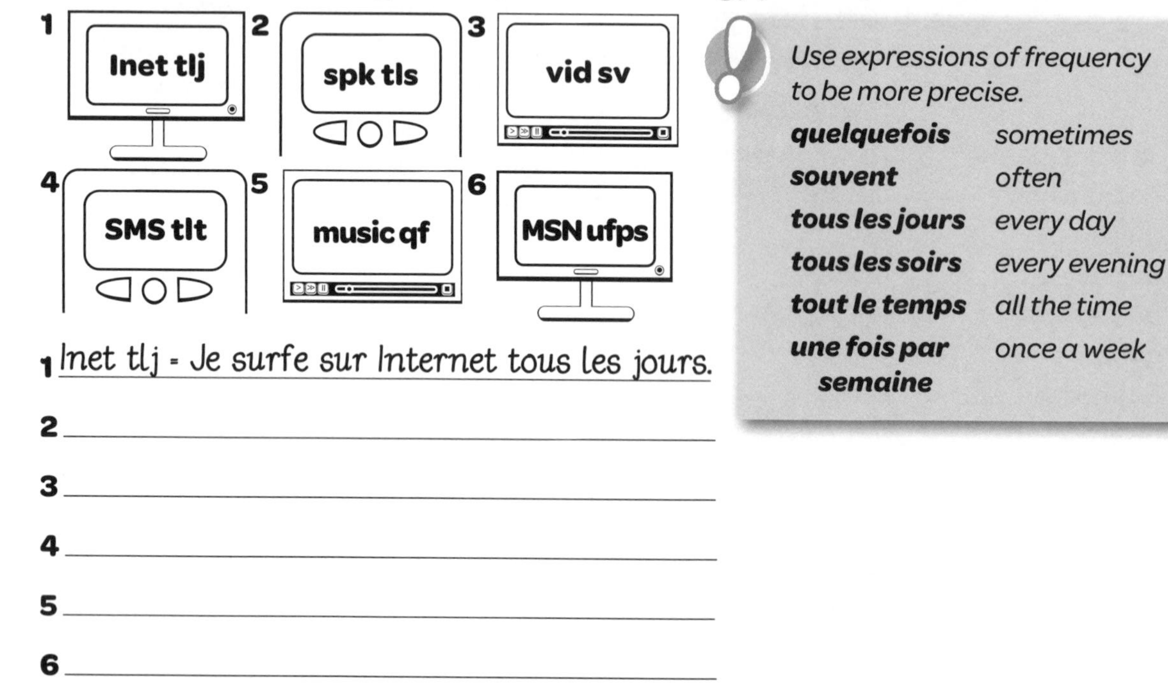

Use expressions of frequency to be more precise.

quelquefois	*sometimes*
souvent	*often*
tous les jours	*every day*
tous les soirs	*every evening*
tout le temps	*all the time*
une fois par semaine	*once a week*

3 **Write a paragraph saying how often you use technology.**

2 Tu es sportif/sportive? (pages 52–53)

1 Unjumble Alice Active's sentences.

1. très suis sportive je Oui,
2. joue Je au la sur tennis Wii
3. hockey le J'adore surtout le sport
4. au basket copains Je avec joue mes
5. joue avec à pétanque mes la Je parents
6. avec Je au joue mes football amis
7. Je fois joue deux volleyball par au semaine
8. sportive est préférée Bartoli Ma Marion

2 Match six of Alice's answers in exercise 1 with these questions.

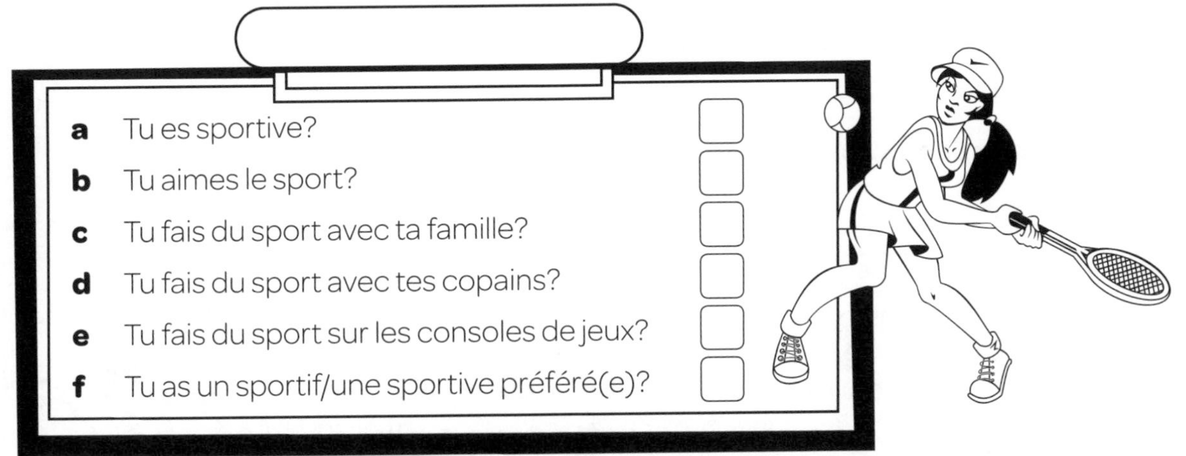

a	Tu es sportive?	☐
b	Tu aimes le sport?	☐
c	Tu fais du sport avec ta famille?	☐
d	Tu fais du sport avec tes copains?	☐
e	Tu fais du sport sur les consoles de jeux?	☐
f	Tu as un sportif/une sportive préféré(e)?	☐

3 Paul Paresseux is lazy and not sporty. Imagine you are Paul and write five sentences to say what you do not do.

To say what someone does not do, put ***ne ... pas*** *around the verb:*

Je ***ne*** *suis* ***pas*** *...*

Je ***ne*** *joue* ***pas*** *...*

Je ***ne*** *fais* ***pas*** *...*

Je ***n'****aime* ***pas*** *...*

Qu'est-ce que tu fais? (pages 54–55)

1 **Complete Suzie Sportive's text with *du/de la/de l'/des*.**

Studio Grammaire

Use *faire de* to talk about sports.

masculine singular	feminine singular	before vowel	plural
***du** roller*	***de la** natation*	***de l'**équitation*	***des** promenades*

Je fais du sport

Lundi 25 novembre

Oui, je fais beaucoup de sport!
En été, je fais **1** ______ natation et je fais souvent **2** ______ vélo avec mes copains. En hiver, je fais **3** ______ patin à glace et je fais **4** ______ danse. Quand il fait beau, je fais **5** ______ équitation ou je fais **6** ______ promenades. J'adore ça! Mais quand il pleut, je fais **7** ______ judo ou quelquefois, je fais **8** ______ roller. Tu aimes le sport?

2 **Read the text in exercise 1 again and answer these questions.**

What does Suzie do when:

1 it's raining? ______________

2 it's winter? ______________

3 it's fine? ______________

4 it's summer? ______________

3 **Complete Samuel's reply with words from the box below.**

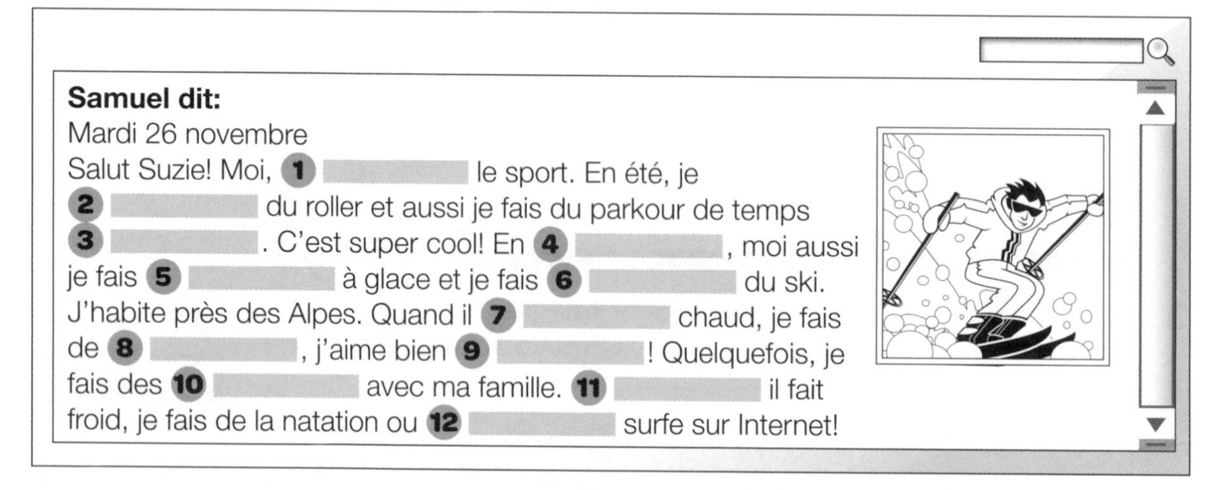

Samuel dit:
Mardi 26 novembre
Salut Suzie! Moi, **1** ______ le sport. En été, je **2** ______ du roller et aussi je fais du parkour de temps **3** ______. C'est super cool! En **4** ______, moi aussi je fais **5** ______ à glace et je fais **6** ______ du ski. J'habite près des Alpes. Quand il **7** ______ chaud, je fais de **8** ______, j'aime bien **9** ______! Quelquefois, je fais des **10** ______ avec ma famille. **11** ______ il fait froid, je fais de la natation ou **12** ______ surfe sur Internet!

fais	*en temps*	*du patin*	*promenades*	*hiver*
aussi	*la natation*	*ça*	*je*	*Quand*	*j'adore*	*fait*

4 J'aime faire ça! (pages 56–57)

1 Crack the code to find out what these people like doing. Remember to add accents.

1. l'zhld sdkdogmdq z ldr bnohmdr. ____________
2. l'zhld sqzhmdq zudb ldr bnozhmr. ____________
3. l'zhld qdsqntudq ldr bnohmdr dm uhkkd. ____________
4. l'zhld ezhqd kdr lzfzrhmr. ____________
5. l'zhld intdq zt ennsazkk. ____________
6. l'zhld dbntsdq cd kz ltrhptd. ____________

2 Use the words in the box to change one item in each of the sentences in exercise 1.

*Example: J'aime jouer **au football**.* → J'aime jouer au tennis.

____
____
____
____
____
____

mes amis	*mon frère*
au tennis	*au basket*
ma mère	*du metal*
de la guitare	*du sport*

3 Rewrite the passage below to make it more interesting by adding connectives and time phrases from the box.

J'aime retrouver mes copines en ville. J'aime faire les magasins. J'aime écouter de la musique. J'aime jouer avec ma Wii. J'aime traîner avec mes amis. J'aime regarder la télévision. J'aime jouer au billard. J'aime faire de la natation.

et	*and*
et j'aime aussi	*and I also like*
le soir	*in the evening*
le weekend	*at the weekend*
le samedi matin	*on Saturday mornings*
le dimanche après-midi	*on Sunday afternoons*
le lundi soir	*on Monday evenings*

Le samedi matin, j'aime retrouver mes copines en ville **et j'aime aussi** ____________

____

____
____
____
____

Ils sont actifs! (pages 58–59)

1 Read the text and number the topics listed below in the order they are mentioned. Then write one thing in English about Ian for each topic.

Mon sportif préféré est Ian Mahinmi. Il joue au basket pour une équipe aux Etats-Unis, San Antonio Spurs. Il est français (il est né le 5 novembre 1986 à Rouen), et il est très grand (2 mètres 11 centimètres) et très beau.

Il a les cheveux courts et noirs et les yeux marron. Il est branché et généreux.

Le soir, il aime jouer sur sa PlayStation et regarder la télé. De temps en temps, le weekend, il fait de la natation ou, quelquefois, il fait les magasins … mais il n'aime pas ça!

Les joueurs de Spurs sont très actifs. Ils s'entraînent cinq ou six fois par semaine. Ils font du jogging et ils font aussi de la musculation. Ils ont un ou deux matchs par semaine. Quelquefois, pour s'entraîner, ils jouent au volley ou au foot.

a personality ☐ *generous*

b physical appearance ☐ ____

c evening activities ☐ ____

d training ☐ ____

e team ☐ ____

f other sports ☐ ____

g where he was born ☐ ____

> ***ils*** *= they (male or mix of male/female)*
>
> ***elles*** *= they (female)*
>
> *The* ***ils/elles*** *form of verbs normally ends in* ***–ent****:*
>
> ***ils jouent*** *they play*
>
> *But it ends in* ***–ont*** *for some irregular verbs:*
>
> ***ils ont*** *they have*
>
> ***ils sont*** *they are*
>
> ***ils font*** *they do*

2 Write a sentence for each picture using *ils* or *elles*.

1 *Ils jouent au basket.*

2 ____

3 ____

4 ____

5 ____

3 Adapt the text in exercise 1 to write about another sportsperson.

Révision 1

1 Throw a die for each row and circle the expression you get.

	⚀	⚁	⚂	⚃	⚄	⚅
Le soir, je ...	 *surfe sur Internet*	 *tchatte sur MSN*	 *télécharge de la musique*	 *envoie des e-mails*	 *regarde des clips vidéo*	 *envoie des SMS*
Le weekend, je joue au ...		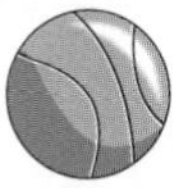		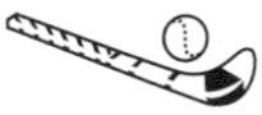		
Quand il fait beau, je ...	*fais du roller*	*fais de l'équitation*	*fais du vélo*	*fais des promenades*	*fais du skate*	*fais du parkour*
Quand il fait froid, je ...	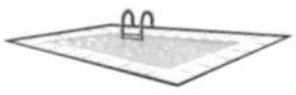					
Le samedi, j'aime ...	*retrouver mes copains en ville*	*faire les magasins*	*jouer sur ma PlayStation*	*écouter de la musique*	*téléphoner à mes copains*	*traîner avec mes copains*
Le dimanche, j'aime ...						

2 Write a paragraph with your circled phrases.

*Add extra details if you can, such as connectives (**et, mais ...**), frequency expressions (**quelquefois ...**) and extra time phrases (**le soir ...**). (See Vocabulaire on pages 30–31 for a list.)*

3 Throw the die again and write a paragraph using *il/elle* (he/she) instead of *je*.

1 **Read the interview. Write the four questions from the box below into the correct spaces.**

Enzo a dix-neuf ans et son sport préféré est le parkour.

Enzo, ______________________

Oui, je fais du parkour tous les weekends et quelquefois aussi le soir. Je fais du parkour en groupe avec des copains. C'est hypercool!

____

J'habite à Paris et je fais du parkour à la Défense, un quartier de Paris. À la Défense, il y a beaucoup d'obstacles.

____

Je n'aime pas le foot et je n'aime pas le rugby mais j'aime les sports extrêmes. J'adore surtout le snowboard. C'est un peu dangereux!

____

Le soir, j'aime jouer sur ma Xbox et j'aime écouter de la musique. J'adore le hip-hop. Le weekend, j'aime traîner avec mes copains.

Tu aimes aussi d'autres sports?	*Qu'est-ce que tu fais pour te relaxer?*
Où fais-tu du parkour?	*Fais-tu souvent du parkour?*

2 **Correct the mistake in each of these sentences. Look carefully at the detail!**

1 Enzo is 18. ______________________

2 He does parkour some weekends. ______________________

3 He also does parkour every evening. ______________________

4 He does it alone. ______________________

5 In La Défense, there aren't many obstacles. ______________________

6 He likes traditional sports. ______________________

7 In the afternoons, he plays on his Xbox. ______________________

8 At the weekend, he likes going into town. ______________________

3 **Look at the interview in exercise 1 again and find the French for these expressions. You may not know all the words, but you should be able to work them out.**

1 favourite sport ______________________

2 every weekend ______________________

3 in a group ______________________

4 an area of Paris ______________________

5 a bit dangerous ______________________

6 in order to relax ______________________

7 other sports ______________________

8 really great ______________________

J'avance

1 **Record your levels for Module 3.**

2 **Look at the level descriptors on pages 60–61 and set your targets for Module 4.**

3 **Fill in what you need to do to achieve these targets.**

Listening	I have reached Level _____ in **Listening**. In Module 4, I want to reach Level _____. I need to ______________________________
Speaking Salut!	I have reached Level _____ in **Speaking**. In Module 4, I want to reach Level _____. I need to ______________________________
Reading	I have reached Level _____ in **Reading**. In Module 4, I want to reach Level _____. I need to ______________________________
Writing	I have reached Level _____ in **Writing**. In Module 4, I want to reach Level _____. I need to ______________________________

Les ordinateurs et les portables • *Computers and mobile phones*

Qu'est-ce que tu fais ...	*What do you do/ are you doing ...*
avec ton ordinateur?	*on your computer?*
avec ton portable?	*on your mobile phone?*
Je joue.	*I play/I'm playing games.*
Je surfe sur Internet.	*I surf/I'm surfing the net.*
Je tchatte sur MSN.	*I chat/I'm chatting on MSN.*
Je regarde des clips vidéo.	*I watch/I'm watching video clips.*
Je télécharge de la musique.	*I download/I'm downloading music.*
J'envoie des SMS.	*I text/I'm texting.*
Je parle avec mes ami(e)s/mes copains/mes copines.	*I talk/I'm talking to my friends/mates.*
J'envoie des e-mails.	*I send/I'm sending e-mails.*

La fréquence • *Frequency*

quelquefois	*sometimes*
souvent	*often*
tous les jours	*every day*
tous les soirs	*every evening*
tout le temps	*all the time*
de temps en temps	*from time to time*
une fois par semaine	*once a week*
deux fois par semaine	*twice a week*

Le sport • *Sport*

Je joue ...	*I play ...*
au basket	*basketball*
au billard	*billiards/snooker*
au foot(ball)	*football*
au hockey	*hockey*
au rugby	*rugby*
au tennis	*tennis*
au tennis de table/ au ping-pong	*table tennis*
au volleyball	*volleyball*
à la pétanque/ aux boules	*boules*
sur la Wii	*on the Wii*
Tu es sportif/ sportive?	*Are you sporty?*
Je suis (assez) sportif/sportive.	*I'm (quite) sporty.*
Je ne suis pas (très) sportif/sportive.	*I'm not (very) sporty.*
Mon sportif/Ma sportive préféré(e) est ...	*My favourite sportsman/ sportswoman is ...*

Qu'est-ce que tu fais? • *What do you do?*

Je fais du judo.	*I do judo.*
Je fais du parkour.	*I do parkour.*
Je fais du patin à glace.	*I go ice-skating.*
Je fais du roller.	*I go roller-skating.*
Je fais du skate.	*I go skateboarding.*
Je fais du vélo.	*I go cycling.*
Je fais de la danse.	*I do dance.*
Je fais de la gymnastique	*I do gymnastics.*
Je fais de la natation.	*I go swimming.*
Je fais de l'équitation.	*I go horse-riding.*
Je fais des promenades.	*I go for walks.*

Vocabulaire

Quand? • *When?*

en été	*in summer*
en hiver	*in winter*
quand il fait beau	*when it's good weather*
quand il fait chaud	*when it's hot*
quand il pleut	*when it rains*
quand il fait froid	*when it's cold*

Qu'est-ce que tu aimes faire? • *What do you like doing?*

le soir	*in the evenings*
le weekend	*at the weekends*
le samedi matin	*on Saturday mornings*
le samedi après-midi	*on Saturday afternoons*
le samedi soir	*on Saturday evenings*
J'aime ...	*I like ...*
... retrouver mes amis en ville.	*... meeting my friends in town.*
... regarder la télévision (la télé).	*... watching TV.*
... jouer sur ma PlayStation.	*... playing on my PlayStation.*
... écouter de la musique.	*... listening to music.*
... faire les magasins.	*... going shopping.*
... faire du sport.	*... doing sport.*
... jouer au football.	*... playing football.*
... traîner avec mes copains.	*... hanging out with my mates.*
... téléphoner à mes copines.	*... phoning my mates.*

Qu'est-ce qu'ils font? • *What do they do?*

Il fait de la lutte.	*He does wrestling.*
Elle fait du jogging.	*She goes jogging.*
Elle a gagné le match.	*She won the match.*
Il est champion régional.	*He's the regional champion.*
Elle s'entraîne (trois) fois par semaine.	*She trains (three) times a week.*
Ils font de la musculation.	*They do weight training.*
Elles écoutent de la musique.	*They listen to music.*
Ils jouent au foot.	*They play football.*
Elles regardent la télé.	*They watch TV.*
Ils sont des clowns.	*They're clowns.*
Elles aiment le R&B.	*They like R&B.*

Les mots essentiels • *High-frequency words*

sur	*on*
en (été)	*in (summer)*
quand	*when*
tout/toute/tous/toutes	*all*
par (deux fois par semaine)	*per (twice a week)*
d'habitude	*usually*
d'abord	*first of all*
ensuite	*then/next*
puis	*then/next*

1 Là où j'habite (pages 70–71)

1 **Read the speech bubbles below and look at the table. Work out who is speaking in each bubble and write their name in the space below.**

Ahmed			✗		✓	✓	✓	✓
Camille	✓		✓	✓		✗		✗
Nathan	✗	✓	✗		✗		✓	
Jade		✓		✓	✓	✗		✗

1

J'habite à Aulnay. C'est une très petite ville. Il y a une église et des cafés. Le vendredi, il y a un marché mais il n'y a pas de piscine et il n'y a pas de stade. Je pense que c'est un peu ennuyeux.

____

2

Moi, j'habite à Cognac. J'aime bien. Il y a des magasins et il y a une piscine. Il y a aussi un stade et des églises mais il n'y a pas de patinoire. Je pense que c'est super!

____

2 **Write speech bubbles for the remaining two people in the table. Make up the town names.**

Il y a un .../une .../des ...	*There is a .../There are ...*
Il n'y a pas de ...	*There isn't a .../There are no ...*

J'habite à ______________________

____

J'habite à ______________________

____

3 **Answer this question to write about your own town/village.**

Tu aimes ta ville/ton village?

Perdu dans le parc d'attractions!

(pages 72–73)

1 Fill in the crossword by completing the sentences below. Use the words in the box to help you.

Studio Grammaire
*tu tourn**es***
*vous tourn**ez***

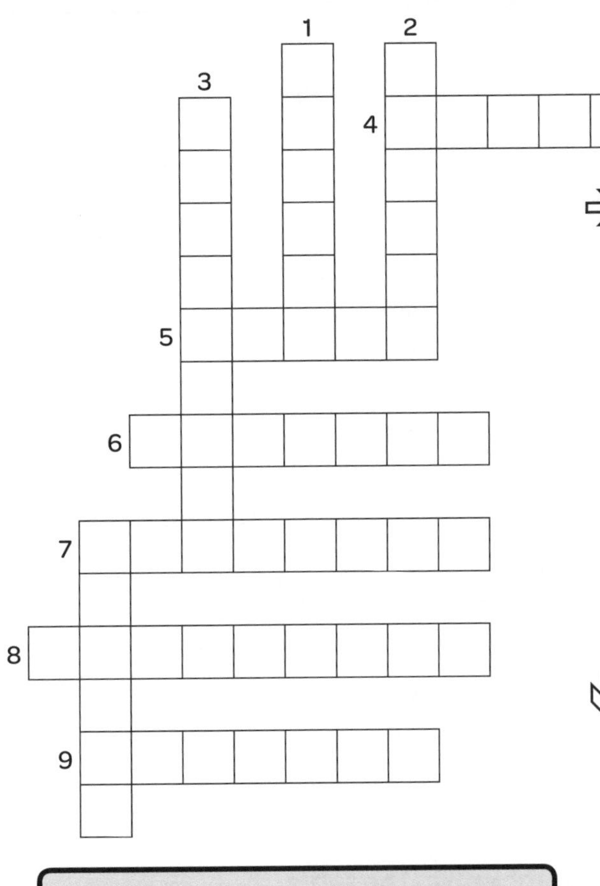

tournes tournez tout droit
devant derrière allez entre
gauche droite carrefour

→
4 Vous ___________ tout droit.
5 L'hôtel est [picture] le café et la piscine.
6 Tu ___________ à droite.
7 Tu passes [picture] le café.
8 Vous allez [picture].
9 Vous ___________ à droite.

↓
1 Tu passes [picture] le cinéma.
2 Tu tournes à [picture].
3 Au [picture], tu vas tout droit.
7 Vous tournez à 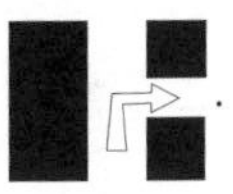.

2 Read Dracula's note giving directions to his castle and draw a mini-diagram. Then write a similar note to your own 'castle'.

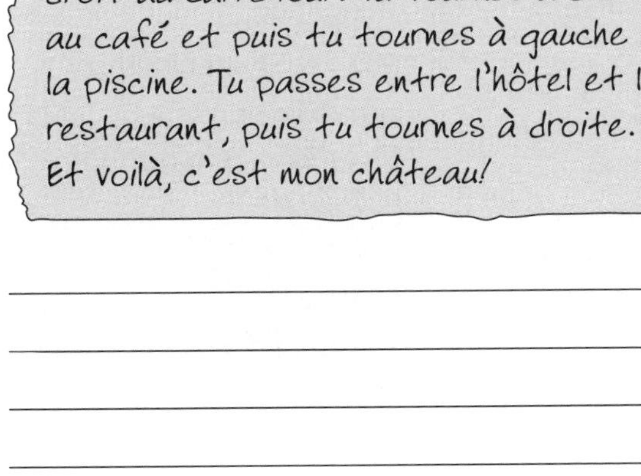

Pour arriver à mon château, tu vas tout droit au carrefour. Tu tournes à droite au café et puis tu tournes à gauche à la piscine. Tu passes entre l'hôtel et le restaurant, puis tu tournes à droite. Et voilà, c'est mon château!

____
____
____
____

1 **Read the forum entries and complete the table below.**

Qu'est-ce que tu fais le weekend?

1 Normalement, le weekend, je vais au centre commercial avec ma mère. J'aime ça, c'est bien!

2 Quelquefois, le dimanche, je vais à l'église avec mes parents. C'est intéressant.

3 D'habitude, le samedi, je vais au centre de loisirs avec mes copains. On joue au volleyball et au basket. C'est super, j'adore ça.

4 Quelquefois, le samedi, je vais à la patinoire avec ma sœur et mon frère. Je n'aime pas ça. C'est difficile.

	How often?	When?	Where?	Who with?	Opinion
1					
2					
3					
4					
5	usually	on Sundays	shops	my friends	great – like it

2 **Write an entry to go with the details for number 5 in the table.**

____

____

3 **Complete this text with *au, à la, à l'* or *aux*. Check on pages 40–41 whether each word is masculine, feminine or plural.**

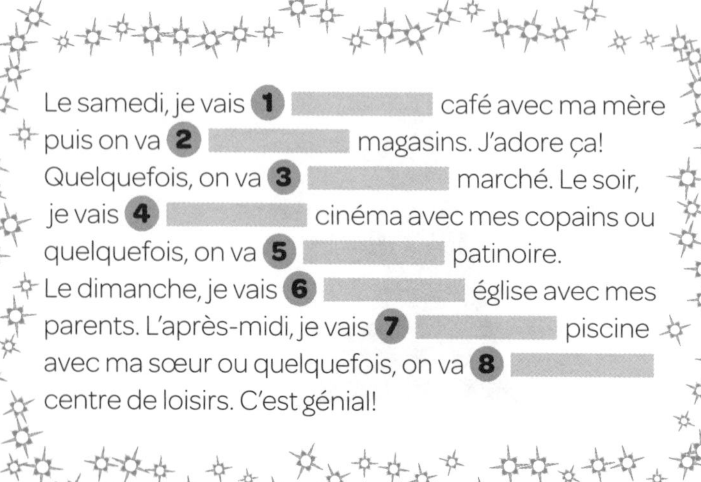

Le samedi, je vais **1** ______ café avec ma mère puis on va **2** ______ magasins. J'adore ça! Quelquefois, on va **3** ______ marché. Le soir, je vais **4** ______ cinéma avec mes copains ou quelquefois, on va **5** ______ patinoire. Le dimanche, je vais **6** ______ église avec mes parents. L'après-midi, je vais **7** ______ piscine avec ma sœur ou quelquefois, on va **8** ______ centre de loisirs. C'est génial!

Studio Grammaire

To say 'to the':

masculine
à + **le** → **au** cinéma

feminine
à + **la** → **à la** patinoire

vowel
à + **l'** → **à l'**église

plural
à + **les** → **aux** magasins

1 Write the jumbled sentences in the correct order.

Marine: **aujourd'hui sortir Veux-tu ?**
1 ______________________________
Tom: Oui, peut-être.
Marine: **matin Tu aller à piscine veux samedi la ?**
2 ______________________________
Tom: Non merci, je n'ai pas envie.
Marine: **aller cinéma Tu samedi veux au soir ?**
3 ______________________________
Tom: Non merci, c'est ennuyeux.
Marine: **patinoire veux à dimanche la Tu matin aller ?**
4 ______________________________
Tom: Non merci, je n'aime pas ça.
Marine: **veux après-midi au Tu centre aller commercial dimanche ?**
5 ______________________________
Tom: Non, c'est vraiment nul.
Marine: Alors, on reste à la maison et … **Internet soir on dimanche sur surfe ?**
6 ______________________________
Tom: Super! Bonne idée!

Marine Marrant

Tom Techno

2 Read the conversation again and draw lines to match the ideas, the times of day and the replies.

Go out	Sunday morning	Good idea!
Go to the swimming pool	Saturday evening	Perhaps.
Go to the cinema	Sunday evening	I don't want to.
Go to the ice rink	Today	I don't like that.
Go to the shopping centre	Saturday morning	It's really rubbish.
Surf the net	Sunday afternoon	It's boring.

3 Write a similar conversation using these symbols.

Théo **Jade**

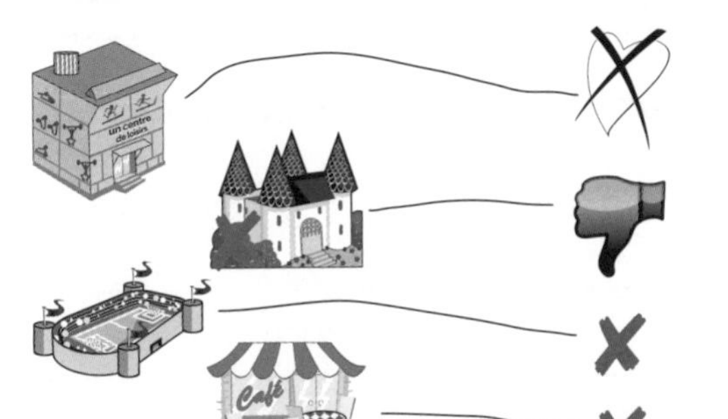

don't like that
don't want to
boring
rubbish
good idea

Tu veux …?
regarder la télé
aller au château
aller au café
aller au stade
aller au centre de loisirs

1 Number the lines of these texts about a town/village in the correct order. Then write them out in the correct order.

Use these clues to help you work out the order.

- *Look at the meaning: what makes sense?*
- *Look at the last word of each line. What words could follow? For example, after* ***des*** *you need a plural noun; after* ***un/une*** *you need a singlar noun.*
- *How can you tell which is the first and last sentence of the paragraph?*

A

magasins, des musées et une	☐	______
bowling ou on peut aller	☐	______
J'habite à Montpellier. C'est	☐	______
au concert. J'adore habiter ici.	☐	______
une grande ville. Il y a des	☐	______
patinoire. On peut faire du	☐	______

B

du skate. On peut aussi jouer	☐	______
très petit village. Il y a un	☐	______
faire du vélo et on peut faire	☐	______
J'habite à Nulvillage. C'est un	☐	______
au flipper au café. C'est un peu ennuyeux.	☐	______
café et une église. On peut	☐	______

2 Write a short paragraph similar to those in exercise 1 using these prompts.

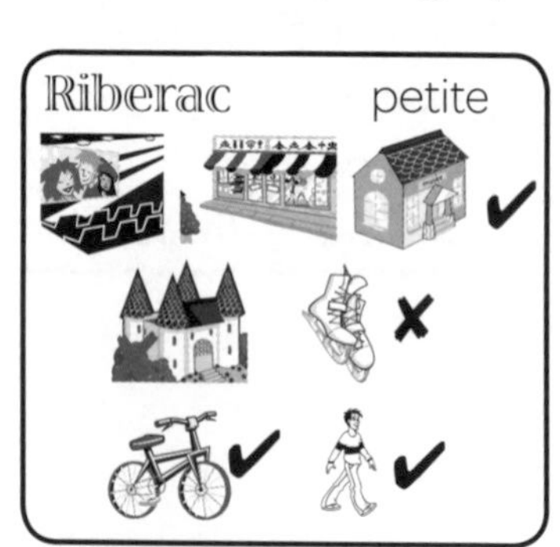

J'habite à ...
C'est ...
Il y a ...
On peut ...

Complete the text below using the words in the box.
Write the words in the crossword.

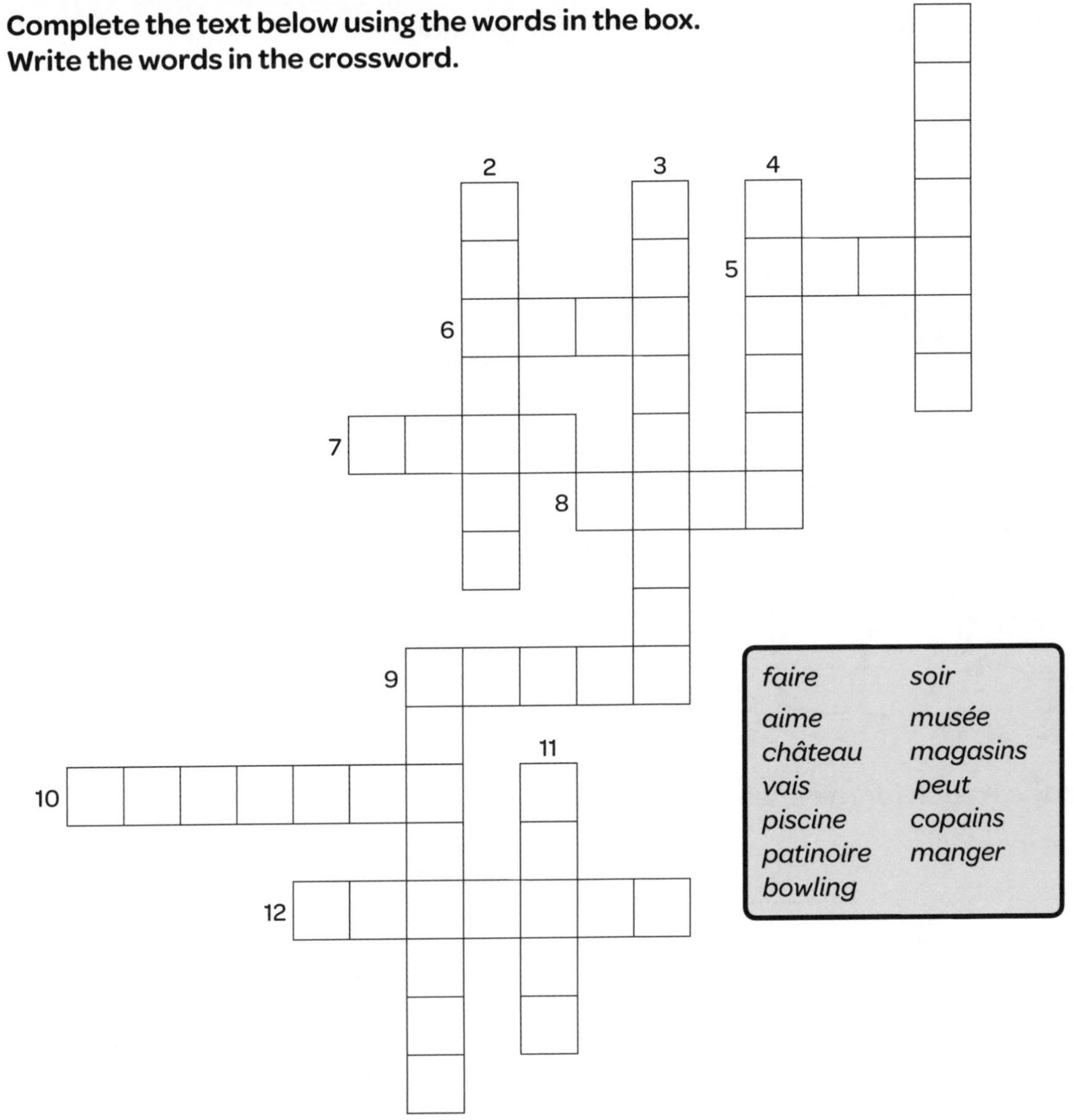

faire, *soir*, *aime*, *musée*, *château*, *magasins*, *vais*, *peut*, *piscine*, *copains*, *patinoire*, *manger*, *bowling*

Moi, j'habite à Superville! Il y a une (**3↓**) 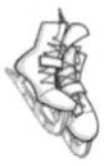 et une (**12→**) 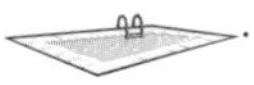.

Il y a beaucoup de (**9↓**) 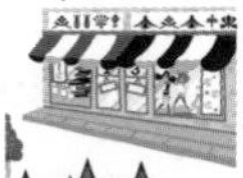. J' (**5→**)  ça.

Mais il n'y a pas de (**1↓**) 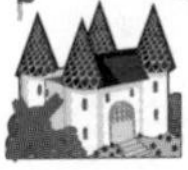 et il n'y a pas de (**9→**) 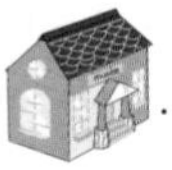.

D'habitude, le weekend, je (**7→**) ________ aux magasins avec mes (**2↓**) 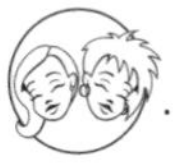.

Quelquefois, je vais au cinéma le samedi (**8→**) 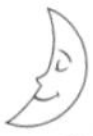.

À Superville, c'est bien. On peut faire du (**10→**) 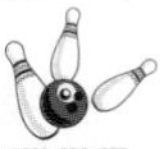 ou on peut (**11↓**) 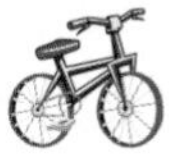 du vélo.

On (**6→**) ________ aller au concert ou (**4↓**) 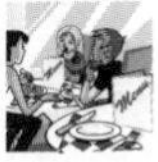 au restaurant.

1 **Read the text about the celebrities in the jungle and:**

- underline four opinions
- circle two times of day
- highlight one sporty activity
- put a wiggly line under two infinitives (e.g. *jouer*).

Salut! Je suis chanteur et en ce moment, j'habite dans la jungle avec dix autres célébrités. C'est pour une émission de télé. C'est très intéressant!
Il n'y a pas de café ou de restaurant. Il n'y a pas de piscine, il n'y a pas de télé et il n'y a pas d'hôtel ... Seulement l'hôtel de la jungle!
Normalement, le matin, je vais à la rivière et je fais de la natation. J'adore ça!
Dans la jungle, on peut manger du riz ... Du riz, du riz, tous les jours! Beurk! Je n'aime pas ça. C'est dégoûtant!
Dans la jungle, on peut faire des promenades ou on peut parler avec les autres célébrités. Le soir, quelquefois, on chante. C'est super!

2 **Find the French for these words and expressions.**

1 at the moment ________________
2 celebrities ________________
3 TV programme ________________
4 the jungle hotel ________________
5 the river ________________
6 rice ________________
7 disgusting ________________
8 we sing ________________

> *Use strategies to find new words, e.g. you may not know the word for 'rice', but you do know that **manger** means 'to eat', so look for something mentioned with **manger** which may be rice.*

3 **Read the text again and answer these questions in English.**

1 What is the writer's normal job/profession? ________________
2 Name three things that he says they don't have in the jungle. ________________
____
3 When does he go to the river? ________________
4 What does he do there and what does he think of it? ________________
5 What does he say they can do in the jungle? (2 things) ________________
____
6 What do they do in the evening? ________________

J'avance

1 Record your levels for Module 4.

2 Look at the level descriptors on pages 60–61 and set your targets for Module 5.

3 Fill in what you need to do to achieve these targets.

Listening	I have reached Level ____ in **Listening**. In Module 5, I want to reach Level ____. I need to ______________________________ ______________________________ ______________________________ ______________________________
Speaking Salut!	I have reached Level ____ in **Speaking**. In Module 5, I want to reach Level ____. I need to ______________________________ ______________________________ ______________________________ ______________________________
Reading	I have reached Level ____ in **Reading**. In Module 5, I want to reach Level ____. I need to ______________________________ ______________________________ ______________________________ ______________________________
Writing	I have reached Level ____ in **Writing**. In Module 5, I want to reach Level ____. I need to ______________________________ ______________________________ ______________________________ ______________________________

Là où j'habite • *Where I live*

Qu'est-ce qu'il y a ... ?	*What is there ... ?*
Il y a ...	*There is ...*
un café	*a café*
un centre commercial	*a shopping centre*
un centre de loisirs	*a leisure centre*
un château	*a castle*
un cinéma	*a cinema*
une église	*a church*
un hôtel	*a hotel*
un marché	*a market*
un parc	*a park*
un restaurant	*a restaurant*
un stade	*a stadium*
une patinoire	*an ice rink*
une piscine	*a swimming pool*
des magasins	*shops*
des musées	*museums*
Il n'y a pas de ...	*There isn't a ... / There are no ...*

Les opinions • *Opinions*

Tu aimes ta ville/ Tu aimes ton village?	*Do you like your town Do you like your village?*
Je pense que ...	*I think that ...*
À mon avis, ...	*In my view, ...*
C'est ...	*It's ...*
bien	*good*
super	*great*
joli	*pretty*
intéressant	*interesting*
ennuyeux	*boring*
vraiment nul	*really rubbish*
trop petit	*too small*
J'aime ça.	*I like that.*
J'adore ça.	*I love that.*
Tu es d'accord?	*Do you agree?*
Oui, je suis d'accord.	*Yes, I agree.*
Non, je ne suis pas d'accord.	*No, I disagree.*

Les directions • *Directions*

Pardon ...	*Excuse me ...*
Où est ... ?	*Where is ... ?*
Où sont ... ?	*Where are ... ?*
C'est ...	*It's ...*
à gauche	*left*
à droite	*right*
tout droit	*straight on*
au carrefour	*at the crossroads*
entre	*between*
derrière	*behind*
devant	*in front of*

Les attractions • *Attractions*

le bateau pirate	*the pirate ship*
le manège	*the merry-go-round*
le Cheval de Troie	*the Trojan horse*
le petit train	*the little train*
le toboggan géant	*the giant slide*
le trampoline magique	*the magic trampoline*
la grotte mystérieuse	*the mysterious grotto*
la rivière enchantée	*the enchanted river*
la soucoupe volante	*the flying saucer*
l'hôtel	*the hotel*
les autos tamponneuses	*the dodgems*
les chaises volantes	*the flying chairs*

Les adverbes de fréquence	***Expressions of frequency***
d'habitude	*usually*
normalement	*normally*
quelquefois	*sometimes*
tous les weekends	*every weekend*

Coucou!	***Hi there!***
je veux	*I want*
tu veux	*you want* (singular, informal)
il/elle veut	*he/she wants*
on veut	*we want*
nous voulons	*we want*
vous voulez	*you want* (plural/ formal)
ils/elles veulent	*they want*
Bonne idée!	*Good idea!*
Super!	*Fabulous!*
Génial!	*Great!*
D'accord.	*OK.*
Oui, c'est super top.	*Yes, that's really great.*
Oui, je veux bien.	*Yes, I want to.*
Non, je n'ai pas envie.	*No, I don't want to.*
Si tu veux.	*If you want to.*
Non merci.	*No, thanks.*

Qu'est-ce qu'on peut faire à ... ?	***What can you do at/in ... ?***
je peux	*I can*
tu peux	*you can* (singular, informal)
il/elle/on peut	*he/she can/we can*
nous pouvons	*we can*
vous pouvez	*you can* (plural/ formal)
ils/elles peuvent	*they can*
aller au concert	*go to a concert*
faire du bowling	*go bowling*
faire du roller	*go roller-skating*
faire du skate	*go skateboarding*
faire du vélo	*go cycling*
faire une promenade en barque	*go on a boat trip*
jouer au babyfoot et au flipper au café	*play table football and pinball at the café*
manger au restaurant	*eat at a restaurant*
visiter les jardins	*visit gardens*
visiter les monuments	*visit monuments*
visiter les musées	*visit museums*

Les mots essentiels	***High-frequency words***
assez	*quite*
mais	*but*
ou	*or*
puis	*then*
très	*very*

1 Find and write out these words and expressions in the word snake.

1 six countries: aux États-Unis ______________________

____

2 three geographical areas: ______________________

3 three words to say when/how often: ______________________

Nous allons ...

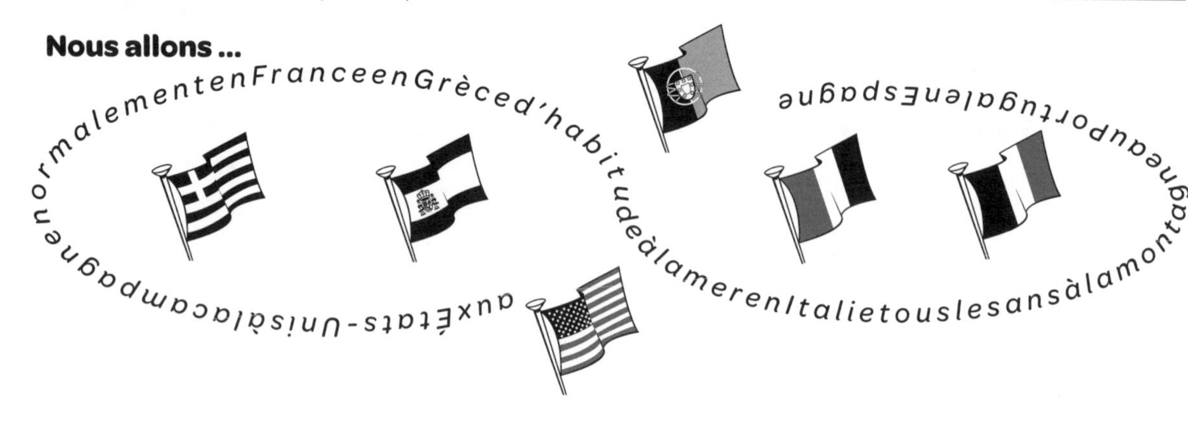

2 Replace the symbols in these sentences with the correct vowels (*a, e, i, o, u*) to find out the holiday activities. Try to add the accents in the right places.

1 N#$s *ll#ns *$ r?st*$r*nt. ______________________

2 N#$s f*@s#ns d? l* r*nd#. ______________________

3 N#$s r?st#ns ?n Fr*nc?. ______________________

4 N#$s v@s@t#ns d?s m#n$m?nts. ______________________

5 N#$s f*@s#ns d? l* n*t*t@#n. ______________________

6 N#$s f*@s#ns d?s *ct@v@t?s sp#rt@v?s. ______________________

7 N#$s f*@s#ns d$ c*mp@ng. ______________________

3 Read the paragraph about what Tom normally does on holiday. Rewrite it, changing the underlined words and phrases to give a different account.

Normalement, nous restons <u>en France</u> mais quelquefois, nous allons <u>en Espagne</u>. Moi, je préfère <u>l'Espagne</u> mais <u>ma mère</u> préfère <u>la France</u>. D'habitude, nous allons <u>à la mer</u> <u>en France</u>. Nous <u>faisons du camping</u>. Quelquefois, nous <u>faisons de la natation</u> ou nous <u>allons au restaurant</u>. J'adore ça, c'est génial!

____

____

____

____

2 Je me prépare ... (pages 92–93)

1 Read what Kalim Kool does to get ready each day and number the pictures in the order they are mentioned in his text.

Le matin, je me prépare, je me fais beau!! Alors ... D'abord, je me douche et je me rase, puis je me lave les dents. Quelquefois, je ne me rase pas mais aujourd'hui, je me rase pour me faire plus beau! Ensuite, je m'habille. Puis je me brosse les cheveux et je me fais une crête. C'est important, ça! Finalement, je me parfume et je me regarde dans la glace. Oui, je suis beau et je suis enfin prêt! J'ai rendez-vous avec ma copine, Camille Cool!

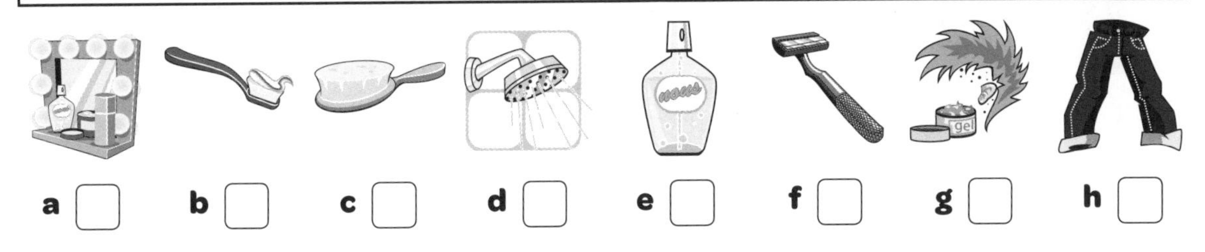

a ☐ **b** ☐ **c** ☐ **d** ☐ **e** ☐ **f** ☐ **g** ☐ **h** ☐

2 Unjumble these sentences about Camille Cool getting ready.

1. dents. douche lave et me je Je me les

   ____

2. me les brosse cheveux. Je

   ____

3. du Je Je mets maquille. me glitter!

   ____

4. Je important, me C'est parfume. ça!

   ____

5. m'habille lunettes et je Je mes de mets soleil.

   ____

6. prête je Voilà, suis!

   ____

Remember that reflexive verbs include a pronoun.
Je me prépare
Tu te douches
Il se rase
To make it negative:
Je ne me rase pas

3 Now use the sentences from exercise 2 to write a paragraph. Make it more structured by using the sequencers in the box.

____

____

____

____

____

d'abord	*first*
ensuite	*next*
puis	*then*
finalement	*finally*

3 Au Café de la Plage (pages 94–95)

1 Read the menu and look at the prices charged (1–8). What item did each person order?

Menu — Café du Port

un café	2,50€
un café-crème	2,90€
un thé	2,80€
un chocolat chaud	2,70€
un jus d'orange	2,95€
une limonade	2,65€
un sandwich au fromage	3,90€
un sandwich au jambon	3,80€
un croquemonsieur	3,55€
une crêpe	3,45€
une glace	3,75€

1. trois euros soixante-quinze ____________
2. deux euros quatre-vingts ____________
3. trois euros quatre-vingt-dix ____________
4. trois euros cinquante-cinq ____________
5. deux euros quatre-vingt-quinze ____________
6. deux euros soixante-cinq ____________
7. trois euros quarante-cinq ____________
8. deux euros soixante-dix ____________

2 Number the lines of this dialogue in an order that makes sense. (There is more than one possibility.) Then adapt it to write your own dialogue. You and your friend are *very* hungry!

Et pour vous, mademoiselle? ☐

Bonjour monsieur, vous désirez? 1

Pour moi, une crêpe et un jus d'orange, s'il vous plaît. ☐

Et comme boisson? ☐

Je voudrais un croquemonsieur, s'il vous plaît. ☐

Un café-crème, s'il vous plaît. ☐

Comme boisson? *What would you like to drink?*

3 Which is the correct total price for all the items metioned in the dialogue above?

treize euros quatre-vingt-cinq ☐	douze euros quatre-vingt-cinq ☐	douze euros quatre-vingt-quinze ☐

Je vais aller en colo! (pages 96–97)

1 Complete the two texts with the words from the boxes.

Pendant les grandes vacances, je **1** ________ aller aux **2** ________ avec ma **3** ________. Je vais **4** ________ à la pêche et je vais **5** ________ dans la mer. Le soir, je vais danser et je vais **6** ________ du karaoké. J'adore ça!

Samuel

nager aller États-Unis faire famille vais

Pendant les **7** ________, je vais **8** ________ en France. Je vais rester au lit jusqu'à onze **9** ________ puis je vais **10** ________ mes copains au centre de loisirs. Je **11** ________ jouer au basket ou je vais **12** ________ dans la piscine. J'adore le sport, c'est génial!

Chloé

heures nager vacances vais retrouver rester

Studio Grammaire

To say what you are **going** to do, use ***aller*** + an infinitive.

Je vais jouer *I'm going to play*

Je vais danser *I'm going to dance*

2 Look at the pictures. Who is it, Samuel or Chloé?

1 ________ 2 ________ 3 ________ 4 ________

5 ________ 6 ________ 7 ________ 8 ________

3 Use these notes to write about your plans for the summer holidays.

go to Spain with family
stay in bed until midday
go swimming in sea
play volleyball
do karaoke

Pendant les vacances je vais ________________

____

____

____

____

1 Look at the pictures below. Find where each idea is mentioned in the texts and write a caption for each picture.

Moi, je voudrais être joueur de basket professionnel. Je voudrais représenter la France aux Jeux paralympiques. Je voudrais faire le tour du monde et jouer au basket aux États-Unis.
Mathis

Un jour, je voudrais aller en Australie. Je voudrais aller à la plage et faire du surf et je voudrais aussi faire de la planche à voile. Je voudrais voir des animaux australiens comme les kangourous et les koalas.
Hugo

Moi, je voudrais être chanteuse professionnelle. J'adore la musique et j'adore chanter. Je voudrais habiter une très grande maison et je voudrais avoir une voiture très cool comme une Porsche.
Camille

Example: Je voudrais représenter la France.

1 ______________________

2 ______________________

3 ______________________

4 ______________________

5 ______________________

6 ______________________

7 ______________________

8 ______________________

2 Choose one item from each box below to write a sentence for each picture.

1 ______________________

2 ______________________

3 ______________________

4 ______________________

5 ______________________

6 ______________________

Je voudrais

rencontrer	*avoir*
aller	*être*
être	*faire*

une voiture très cool	*au Canada*
le tour du monde	*danseuse*
footballeur	*mon acteur préféré*

Révision 1

1 Copy the sentences below into the correct column of the table. Remember to look for patterns.

What you and your family normally do *Normalement, nous ...*	**What you plan to do this weekend** *Ce weekend, je vais ...*	**What you would like to do one day** *Un jour, je voudrais ...*

2 Using the sentences in exercise 1 and the words below, try to translate these sentences into French.

1. Normally, we go to Spain.
2. Normally, we go swimming.
3. This weekend, I'm going to play basketball.
4. This weekend, I'm going to get together with my cousins.
5. One day, I would like to be a professional singer.
6. One day, I would like to go to Canada.

au Canada jouer au basket en Espagne
faire de la natation chanteur/chanteuse mes cousins

Révision 2

1 Read the chat forum about holidays and answer the questions below.

Les vacances

15 juin

À ton avis, c'est bien ou c'est nul?

posté par Caramel

Kiddo76 dit:
Salut! Moi, j'adore les vacances. Pour les vacances, cet été, je vais aller au Portugal. On va nager dans la mer et on va faire de la planche à voile. Mon frère aussi va faire de la voile. C'est super, les vacances!

Yannis80 dit:
À mon avis, les vacances, c'est nul. Un jour, je voudrais faire le tour du monde et je voudrais aller au Canada et aux États-Unis. Je voudrais visiter New York et je voudrais faire les magasins. Je voudrais rencontrer le président des États-Unis.

Buzz.21 dit:
Oui, les vacances, c'est bien en général. D'habitude, nous restons en France et nous allons à la montagne, dans les Pyrénées. Quelquefois, nous visitons l'Espagne parce que c'est tout près des Pyrénées. Nous faisons du camping et nous faisons de la rando tous les jours. J'aime le camping mais je n'aime pas la rando.

Who ...

1. talks about what they **would like** to do? __________
2. talks about what they **usually** do? __________
3. talks about what they are **going** to do? __________
4. does not like holidays? __________
5. loves holidays? __________
6. has mixed feelings about holidays? __________

2 Read the forum again and find the French for these expressions.

1. I'd like to go shopping. __________
2. Sometimes, we visit Spain. __________
3. For the holidays, this summer ... __________
4. We go walking every day. __________
5. I would like to meet the president of the USA. __________
6. Holidays are great! __________

3 Write an entry for the forum above.

J'avance

1 **Record your levels for Module 5.**

2 **Look at the level descriptors on pages 60–61 and set your targets for Module 6.**

3 **Fill in what you need to do to achieve these targets.**

Listening	I have reached Level ____ in **Listening**. In Module 6, I want to reach Level ____. I need to ________________________________ ________________________________ ________________________________ ________________________________
Speaking Salut!	I have reached Level ____ in **Speaking**. In Module 6, I want to reach Level ____. I need to ________________________________ ________________________________ ________________________________ ________________________________
Reading	I have reached Level ____ in **Reading**. In Module 6, I want to reach Level ____. I need to ________________________________ ________________________________ ________________________________ ________________________________
Writing	I have reached Level ____ in **Writing**. In Module 6, I want to reach Level ____. I need to ________________________________ ________________________________ ________________________________ ________________________________

Les vacances en famille • *Family holidays*

Tous les ans ...	*Every year ...*
Normalement ...	*Normally ...*
nous allons ...	*we go ...*
en France	*to France*
en Espagne	*to Spain*
en Grèce	*to Greece*
en Italie	*to Italy*
aux États-Unis	*to the USA*
au Portugal	*to Portugal*
à la mer	*to the seaside*
à la montagne	*to the mountains*
à la campagne	*to the countryside*
Nous allons au restaurant.	*We go to a restaurant.*
Nous visitons des monuments.	*We visit monuments.*
Nous faisons du camping.	*We go camping.*
Nous faisons de la rando.	*We go hiking.*
Nous faisons de la natation.	*We go swimming.*
Nous faisons des activités sportives.	*We do sports activities.*
Nous restons en France.	*We stay in France.*

Je me prépare • *I get myself ready*

Je me douche.	*I have a shower.*
Je me fais une crête.	*I make my hair spiky.*
Je me parfume.	*I put on perfume/ aftershave.*
Je m'habille.	*I get dressed.*
Je me brosse les cheveux.	*I brush my hair.*
Je me lave les dents.	*I clean my teeth.*
Je me regarde dans la glace.	*I look in the mirror.*
Je me rase.	*I shave.*
Je me maquille.	*I put on make-up.*

Les nombres et l'argent • *Numbers and money*

quarante	*40*
quarante-cinq	*45*
cinquante	*50*
cinquante-cinq	*55*
soixante	*60*
soixante-cinq	*65*
soixante-dix	*70*
soixante-quinze	*75*
quatre-vingts	*80*
quatre-vingt-cinq	*85*
quatre-vingt-dix	*90*
quatre-vingt-quinze	*95*
Tu as combien d'argent?	*How much money have you got?*
J'ai dix euros cinquante.	*I've got ten euros fifty (cents).*

Vocabulaire

Au café • *At the café*

J'ai faim et j'ai soif.	*I'm hungry and I'm thirsty.*
Vous désirez?	*What would you like?*
Je voudrais ...	*I'd like ...*
un café	*a black coffee*
un café-crème	*a white coffee*
un thé (au lait/ au citron)	*a tea (with milk/ lemon)*
un chocolat chaud	*a hot chocolate*
un coca	*a cola*
un jus d'orange	*an orange juice*
un Orangina	*an Orangina*
une limonade	*a lemonade*
un sandwich au fromage	*a cheese sandwich*
un sandwich au jambon	*a ham sandwich*
un croquemonsieur	*a toasted cheese and ham sandwich*
une crêpe	*a pancake*
une glace (à la vanille/à la fraise/ au chocolat)	*a (vanilla/strawberry/ chocolate) ice-cream*

Qu'est-ce que tu vas faire? • *What are you going to do?*

Pendant les vacances ...	*During the holidays ...*
je vais ...	*I'm going to ...*
aller à la pêche	*go fishing*
danser	*dance*
faire de l'accrobranche	*do treetop adventures*
faire du karaoké	*do karaoke*
faire de la voile	*go sailing*
faire de la planche à voile	*go windsurfing*
nager dans la mer	*swim in the sea*
rester au lit	*stay in bed*
retrouver mes copains/copines	*get together with with my mates*

Quels sont tes rêves? • *What are your dreams?*

Je voudrais aller ...	*I'd like to go ...*
à Paris	*to Paris*
en Australie	*to Australia*
au Canada	*to Canada*
aux États-Unis	*to the USA*
Je voudrais ...	*I'd like ...*
être footballeur professionnel	*to be a professional football player (masculine)*
être danseuse professionnelle	*to be a professional dancer (feminine)*
habiter dans une grande maison	*to live in a big house*
avoir une voiture très cool	*to have a really cool car*
faire le tour du monde	*to travel around the world*
rencontrer mon acteur/mon actrice préféré(e)	*to meet my favourite actor/actress*

Les mots essentiels • *High-frequency words*

pendant	*during*
combien (de)?	*how much?/how many?*
à	*to/in (+ town)*
en	*to/in (+ feminine country)*
au	*to/in (+ masculine country)*
aux	*to/in (+ plural country)*
d'abord	*first*
ensuite	*next*
puis	*then*
finalement	*finally*
quelquefois	*sometimes*

1 **Read the text quickly for gist. You won't understand everything, but see what you can understand in two minutes. To help you, find the words from the box below and underline them in the text.**

1 La vache ne voit pas les couleurs. Elle voit bien sur les côtés et un peu derrière elle, mais elle ne voit pas très bien juste devant elle.

2 Le chien ne voit pas très bien les couleurs. En particulier, il ne voit pas le rouge. Il voit assez bien sur les côtés et il voit très bien le mouvement.

3 L'aigle voit très bien le rouge, le vert et le bleu. Quand il vole dans le ciel, il voit facilement ses proies. Il ne vole pas la nuit.

4 L'abeille ne voit pas très bien les choses qui sont près d'elle. L'abeille ne voit pas le rouge mais elle voit des couleurs que les humains ne voient pas.

5 La grenouille ne voit pas très bien les formes mais elle voit très bien le mouvement. Elle voit aussi très bien les couleurs.

6 L'escargot ne voit presque rien. Il peut détecter la lumière et les mouvements qui sont près de lui.

voit	*sees*	**facilement**	*easily*	**les formes**	*shapes*
ne voit pas	*does not see*	**ses proies**	*its prey*	**ne … rien**	*nothing*
les côtés	*sides*	**la nuit**	*at night*	**presque**	*hardly*
il vole	*it flies*	**près de**	*near*	**la lumière**	*light*

2 **Match each text in exercise 1 with one of these animals. You may have to guess some of them. Use a dictionary if you need to. Write the name of each animal in French.**

a

☐ ____________

b

☐ ____________

c

☐ ____________

d

☐ ____________

e

☐ ____________

f

☐ ____________

3 **Write the number of each animal from exercise 1.**

Which one:

a can't see red? (two of them) ____________

b can't see shapes very well? ____________

c can see its prey easily? ____________

d can't see very well in front of it? ____________

e sees red, green and blue well? ____________

f can hardly see anything? ____________

g sees colours that humans can't? ____________

h sees quite well to the side? ____________

i does not see colours? ____________

j can detect light? ____________

4 **Complete these summaries of three of the animals.**

The cow **1** ____________ colours. It sees well **2** ____________ and a little **3** ____________, but it **4** ____________ very well just in front of it.

The dog does not see **5** ____________ very well; in particular, it **6** ____________ red. It **7** ____________ to the side and it sees **8** ____________ very well.

The frog does not see **9** ____________ very well, but it sees **10** ____________ very well. It also **11** ____________ colours **12** ____________, too.

5 **Choose another animal and research what it can or can't see. Write a text about it.**

____

____

____

____

____

____

____

Poésie (pages 112–113)

1 Read the poem out loud. Be careful with your pronunciation – some of the lines rhyme!

1 Mon animal préféré
C'est sûrement le tigre
Il est orange, noir avec un peu de blanc,
Il court vite et j'adore ses mouvements
On le trouve en Inde et aussi en Asie
Mais l'homme est bien sûr son ennemi.

2 Mon acteur préféré
C'est Robert Pattinson
Il est beau, il est gentil
Il est charmant, il est poli
J'adore voir ses films au cinéma
Il est cool et il est vraiment sympa.

3 Mon groupe préféré
C'est certainement Muse
Ils jouent bien des instruments
Ils ont beaucoup de talent
J'écoute leur rock à la radio
Et j'adore regarder leurs clips vidéo.

4 Mon sportif préféré
C'est le footballeur Gaël Kakuta
Il joue pour Chelsea en Angleterre
En poste milieu-gauche il est vraiment super
Il est très jeune et très rapide, comme joueur
Et il est extrêmement talentueux, comme footballeur.

2 Read the poem again and answer these questions.

1 What is said about the tiger? (2 things)

____

2 Where can you find the tiger? ______________________________

3 How is Robert Pattinson described? (4 things)

____

4 How does the writer listen to and watch Muse?

____

5 Who is Gaël Kakuta? ______________________________

6 How is he described? (2 things) ______________________________

3 Now you're going to plan your own poem.

- Choose one verse and write out the first line. Then change the second line to talk about your favourite animal/actor/group/sportsperson.
- Look for other sentences that you can adapt, e.g. for the animal, change the names of the countries to say where it lives; for the actor/actress, change the adjectives to say what they're like.
- You don't have to make the lines rhyme, but if you want to, use the rhyming words in the box below.

Rhyming words

éléphant/important
charmant/intelligent
curieux/ennuyeux/généreux
marrant/intéressant
petit/poli/aujourd'hui
judo/vélo/beau
magasins/copains
musique/fantastique
Internet/français

4 Read the text about a famous French poet and fill in the details in the identity card.

Jacques Prévert est un grand poète français.
Il est né le 4 février 1900 à Neuilly-sur-Seine.
Il a écrit beaucoup de poèmes. Il a aussi écrit des scénarios pour le cinéma et il a été membre du groupe des surréalistes avec ses copains Robert Desnos et André Breton.
Il aime bien faire des jeux de mots et il aime inventer des mots. Ses poèmes sont très marrants.
En France les élèves récitent les poèmes de Prévert à l'école primaire et au collège.
Il est décédé à l'âge de soixante-dix-sept ans.

Name: ....
Date of birth: ....
Profession: ....
Writing style: ....
Famous friends: ....
Age he died: ....

il a été *he was*

1 **Read the instructions below to colour in this Matisse-style picture.**

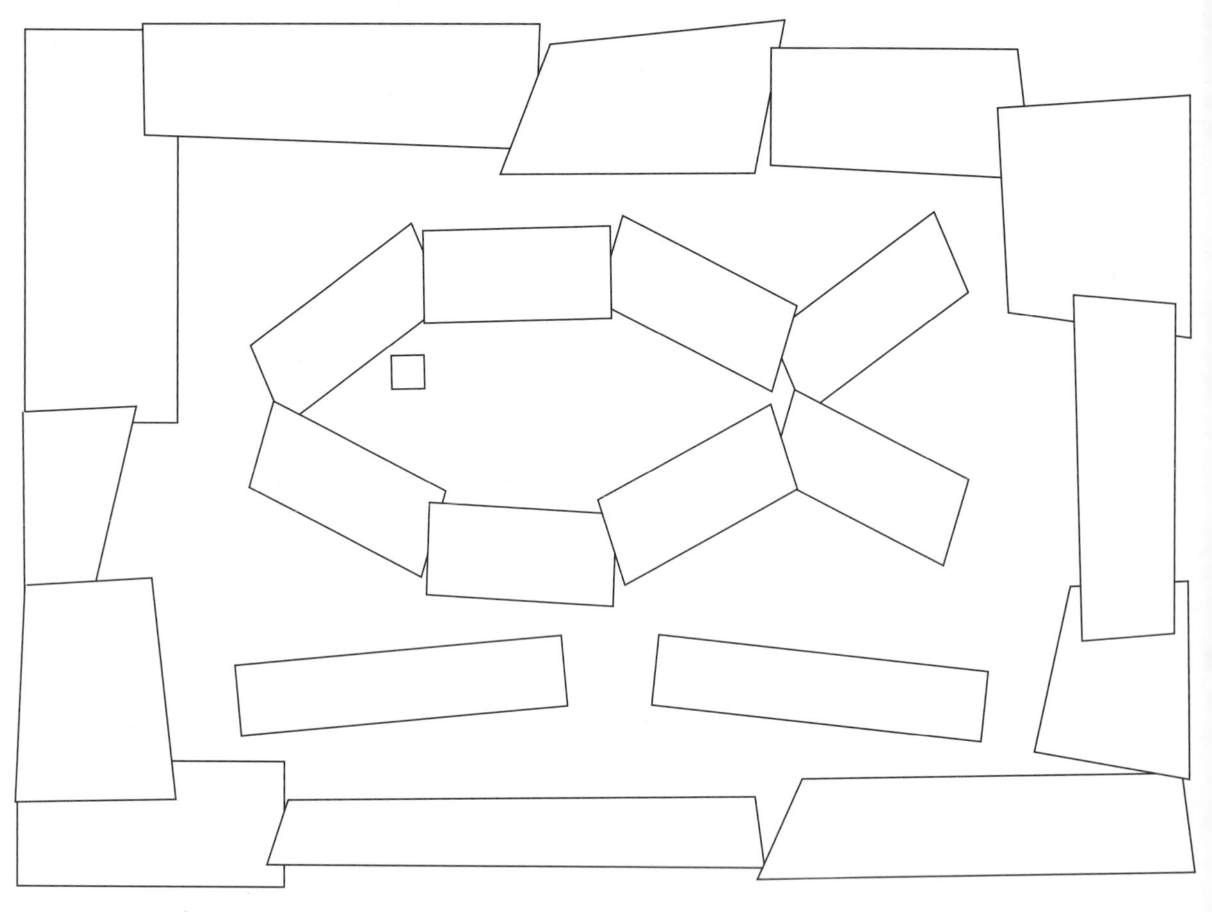

- L'image, c'est un poisson!
- À droite, c'est la queue du poisson. Colorie les rectangles de la queue en jaune et noir.
- Colorie l'œil du poisson en bleu.
- Il y trois rectangles en haut et trois en bas du poisson. Commence à gauche et colorie les trois rectangles du haut en orange, vert et bleu.
- En bas, commence à droite et colorie les rectangles en vert, rouge et rose.
- Il y a un rectangle sous le poisson, à gauche: colorie-le en orange.
- Il y a un rectangle sous le poisson à droite: colorie-le en jaune.
- Colorie le cadre en rouge.

colorie	*colour in*	***en bas***	*at the bottom*
la queue	*tail*	***en haut***	*at the top*
à droite	*on the right*	***sous***	*under*
à gauche	*on the left*	***le cadre***	*frame*
l'œil	*the eye*		

- This painting is in the style of Henri Matisse.
- Matisse was a French painter who lived from 1869 to 1954.
- He loved using bright colours, partly inspired by living in the hot climate of the south of France.
- Later in his career, he created papercut pictures – collages made of brightly painted pieces of paper. One example is the picture called *L'escargot,* which is in the shape of a snail.

2 Follow the instructions to create your own Matisse-style picture. There is space on the next page!

- Choisis un animal, par exemple un chat, un hamster ou peut-être une araignée!
- Dessine la forme de l'animal simplement.
- Dessine des rectangles sur la forme de l'animal.

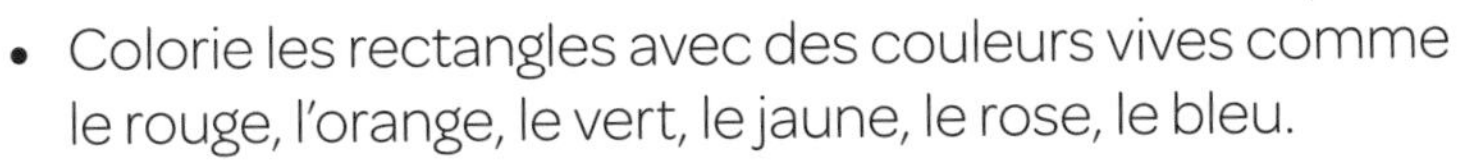

- Colorie les rectangles avec des couleurs vives comme le rouge, l'orange, le vert, le jaune, le rose, le bleu.

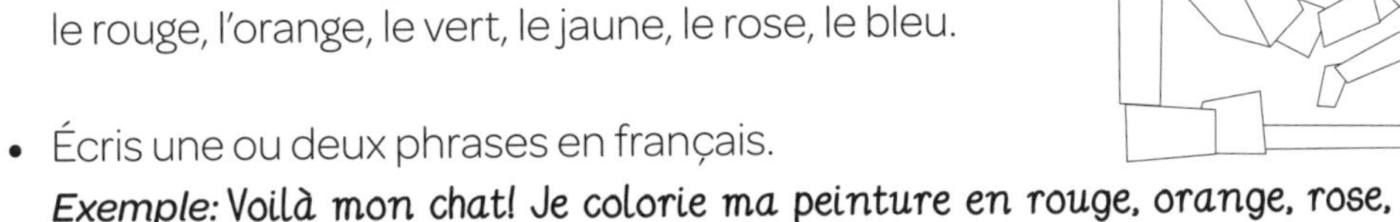

- Écris une ou deux phrases en français.
  Exemple: Voilà mon chat! Je colorie ma peinture en rouge, orange, rose, vert et bleu.
- Voilà, tu as une image dans le style de Matisse!

3 Lucy's research on the painter Claude Monet has got muddled up! Rearrange the words in each sentence so they make sense.

Monet recherches des fait Claude sur J'ai ______

qui 'Le pont japonais' J'ai tableau s'appelle choisi un ______

observé de J'ai beaucoup choses ______

de différentes couleurs identifié beaucoup J'ai ______

tableau J'adore ce ______

surtout les les et J'aime plantes fleurs ______

super vraiment C'est! ______

4 Translate Lucy's research into English.

Create your own Matisse-style picture here.

Record your levels for Module 6.

Listening	I have reached Level ______ in **Listening**.
Speaking	I have reached Level ______ in **Speaking**.
Reading	I have reached Level ______ in **Reading**.
Writing	I have reached Level ______ in **Writing**.

Look back through your workbook and note down the level you achieved in each skill by the end of each Module.

	Listening	**Speaking**	**Reading**	**Writing**
1 C'est perso				
2 Mon collège				
3 Mes passetemps				
4 Ma zone				
5 3 ... 2 ... 1 Partez!				
6 Studio découverte				

You now have a record of your progress in French for the whole year.

Attainment Target 1: Listening and responding

Level 1	I can understand some familiar spoken words and phrases.
Level 2	I can understand a range of familiar spoken phrases.
Level 3	I can understand the main points of short spoken passages and note people's answers to questions.
Level 4	I can understand the main points of spoken passages and some of the detail.
Level 5	I can understand the main points and opinions in spoken passages about different topics. I can recognise if people are speaking about the future **OR** the past as well as the present.

Attainment Target 2: Speaking

Level 1	I can say single words and short phrases.
Level 2	I can answer simple questions and use set phrases.
Level 3	I can ask questions and use short phrases to answer questions about myself.
Level 4	I can take part in conversations. I can express my opinions. I can use grammar to change phrases to say something new.
Level 5	I can give short talks, in which I express my opinions. I can take part in conversations giving information, opinions and reasons. I can speak about the future **OR** the past as well as the present.

Attainment Target 3: Reading and responding

Level	
Level 1	I can understand familiar words and phrases.
Level 2	I can understand familiar phrases. I can read aloud familiar words and phrases. I can use a vocabulary list to check meanings.
Level 3	I can understand the main points and people's answers to questions in short written texts.
Level 4	I can understand the main points in short texts and some of the detail. Sometimes I can work out the meaning of new words.
Level 5	I can understand the main points and opinions in texts about different topics. I can recognise if the texts are about the future **OR** the past as well as the present.

Attainment Target 4: Writing

Level	
Level 1	I can write or copy single words correctly.
Level 2	I can copy short sentences correctly and write some words from memory.
Level 3	I can answer questions about myself. I can write short phrases from memory. I can write short sentences with help.
Level 4	I can write short texts on familiar topics. I can use grammar to change phrases to write something new.
Level 5	I can write short texts on a range of familiar topics. I can write about the future **OR** the past as well as the present.

Notes

Heinemann is an imprint of Pearson Education Limited, a company incorporated in England and Wales, having its registered office at Edinburgh Gate, Harlow, Essex, CM20 2JE. Registered company number: 872828

www.pearsonschoolsandfecolleges.co.uk

Heinemann is a registered trademark of Pearson Education Limited

First published 2010

19
18

British Library Cataloguing in Publication Data
A catalogue record for this book is available from the British Library

ISBN 978 0 435 02780 3

Edited by Catriona Watson-Brown
Designed by Emily Hunter-Higgins
Typeset by HL Studios
Original illustrations © Pearson Education Limited 2010
Illustrated by Caron at KJA Artists
Cover design by Emily Hunter-Higgins
Cover photo © Pearson Education Ltd/Sophie Bluy
Printed in Great Britain by Ashford Colour Press Ltd.

Acknowledgements
The author and publisher would like to thank Bayard Jeunesse for permission to use copyright material:

Animals text © ASTRAPI, BAYARD JEUNESSE p 52

Every effort has been made to contact copyright holders of material reproduced in this book. Any omissions will be rectified in subsequent printings if notice is given to the publishers.

Heinemann is part of
PEARSON

T 0845 630 33 33
F 0845 630 77 77
customer.orders@pearson.com
www.pearsonschools.co.uk

ISBN 978-0-435-02780-3